D0941662

LIFESAVING AND WATER SAFETY TODAY

AQUATIC RESOURCES

Available through Association Press
or Local YMCAs

STUDENT SERIES

It's Fun to Swim the Y's Way, by Harold T. Friermood

PROFESSIONAL SERIES

Adventures in Artificial Respiration, by Peter V. Karpovich

Camp Waterfront Programs and Management, by Richard H. Pohndorf

Fun in the Water, by Thomas K. Cureton, Jr.

Lifesaving and Water Safety Today, by Charles E. Silvia

The New Science of Skin and Scuba Diving, A Project of the Council for National
    Cooperation in Aquatics, Bernard E. Empleton, Chairman Editorial Committee

New YMCA Aquatic Workbook, edited by Harold T. Friermood

*100 Revised and New Questions with Confidential Answers on YMCA Lifesaving and
    Water Safety.* Available to qualified personnel only, through Area/State offices

*Skin and Scuba Diver Training and Leadership Preparation: National Standards for
    Certification*, supplementary unit for the *New YMCA Aquatic Workbook*, edited
    by Harold T. Friermood

OTHER SOURCES OF AQUATIC INFORMATION

American National Red Cross, 18th and E Sts., N.W., Washington, D. C. 20006

Boy Scouts of America, New Brunswick, N. J. 08903

Council for National Cooperation in Aquatics, 1201 16th St., N.W., Washington,
    D. C. 20036

Girl Scouts of the U.S.A., 830 Third Ave., New York, N. Y. 10022

Lifesaving and Water Safety Today

for
Students and Instructors

BY CHARLES E. SILVIA, *Professor of Physical Education*
Springfield College, Springfield, Massachusetts

Editorial Committee:

HAROLD T. FRIERMOOD, *Chairman*

LOUIS A. COX

BERNARD E. EMPLETON

EDWARD L. GRIFFIN

CHARLES E. SILVIA

ASSOCIATION PRESS • NEW YORK

LIFESAVING AND WATER SAFETY TODAY

Dedicated to

THOMAS K. CURETON, JR., PH.D.

HAROLD T. FRIERMOOD, ED.D.

and

MY STUDENTS

Foreword

FOLLOWING the pioneer work of the Royal Humane Society (1774), the Massachusetts Humane Society (1786), and the U.S. Coast Guard Life Saving Service (1871), the YMCA entered the lifesaving field between 1885 and 1890. The United Volunteer Life Saving Corps was organized in 1890. By 1911 the lifesaving work was established at the International YMCA College, at Springfield, Massachusetts. In 1914 the American Red Cross entered the field to train volunteer leaders, especially to serve in emergency floods and rural waters, where paid guards did not exist. More recently, a number of large city recreation departments and public beaches have established their own courses of training to meet very specifically the requirements and scope of their own work.

The YMCA lifesaving program received original impetus from the foresight of Professor William H. Ball, Dr. James H. McCurdy, Professor George B. Affleck, and Dr. George Fisher. The first American book on lifesaving was written by George Goss as a thesis at Springfield College in 1913. The national YMCA lifesaving service was organized in 1912 and the Goss text was published by the Association Press in 1916. The work was originally promoted as "water first aid." In 1916 the YMCA opened the first aquatic school at the Boston YMCA to train leaders in swimming work under the joint direction of Arthur E. Dome and B. Dean Brink. This set the pattern for short term institutes the country over. From 1924 to 1929 the YMCA swimming and lifesaving program went ahead strongly under Dr. John Brown, Jr., Dr. Henry F. Kallenberg, John W. Fuhrer, and George Draper with the development of the *Field Agent's Guide*, a new *YMCA Life Saving and Swimming Manual*, certificates of recognition, and the heroic service medallions. From 1929 the research work of Dr. Peter V. Karpovich, Professor T. K. Cureton, Jr., and various graduate students added greatly to the scholarly understanding of the work. Donald S. Stone (1937) and Charles E. Silvia (1940) completed surveys of the practical methods and all published material on lifesaving as a basis of recommending improvements in the YMCA program. A new lifesaving test booklet was published by Cureton and Silvia in 1939 including theoretical and practical tests. This was adopted as Vol. III in the National YMCA Aquatic Literature Series. The physiology of drowning, comparison of the several methods of resuscitation, methods of respiration, hygienic effects of water on individuals, and a wide assortment of practical methods were tried experimentally. In 1943 Dr. Cureton published his *Warfare Aquatics* which was widely used in the services and in the YMCA institutes of the World War II period. Training courses in this broadened and the more practical program caught on widely. Charles E. Silvia, my protégé and intimate colleague, has carried forward many of these ideas into new writings and revisions of the YMCA lifesaving materials.

Charles E. Silvia has written this latest book on *Lifesaving and Water Safety*

Today for students and instructors, making use of supporting research. It is a scholarly job, based in part on his own extensive historical and practical research work in this field. It covers the theory, irrespective of any organization bias. It stands as the most careful summary ever made. All instructors and students of lifesaving should use it in their study and class work.

Thomas Kirk Cureton, Jr.
*Honorary Chairman of
the National YMCA
Aquatic Committee*

Urbana, Illinois.
January, 1965.

Preface

THE progress of the lifesaving and water-safety phase of the National YMCA Aquatic Program has been noteworthy since the publication of the first edition of this work in 1949. The need, however, for a combined text for both students and instructors has been apparent to the editorial committee for some time in order to achieve a more thorough understanding of this aspect of the total aquatic program. Although standardization of the principles of procedure and technique is essential to the continued growth and development of this program, such standardization should not result in the stifling of the individual instructor's initiative and creativeness. Rote teaching and learning, devoid as they are of curiosity and compelling desire to know "why," are dangerous because of the tendency they have to produce an individual who is unable to think and does not want to think beyond the confines of his teaching. The properly trained lifesaver is a person who has been taught the value of reading the literature of the field and listening to experts, and who has the ability to adapt himself to a wide variety of emergency rescue situations.

The phrase, "lifesaving through watermanship," has been coined by the writer to impress upon teacher and student alike the great importance of basing lifesaving training on the principles of watermanship. These principles in the mind of the writer are: (1) endurance (organic power); (2) breath control (breath-holding and ex-clusion of water from the nose); (3) agility (ability to move quickly); (4) skill (knowledge of techniques); (5) emotional fitness (confidence tempered with humility); and (6) directed aggressiveness. These principles of watermanship are actually achievement goals, and the lifesaver who achieves proficiency in them will respond effectively to the needs of any rescue situation.

The tendency to become involved with the minutiae of the various lifesaving techniques should be curbed because this tendency is usually paralleled with inadequate knowledge of the basic principles.

The techniques illustrated by Figs. 28a, 32, 33a, 33b, 34, 35, 42a, 44a, 47a, 47b, 49, 53, 55a, 55b, 55c, 55d, 56a, 56b, 57a, 57b, 58a, 58b, 59a, 59b, 59c, 59d, 60, 62a, 62b, 62c, 62d, 62e, were developed by the writer and his assistants at Springfield College during the past twenty-five years. Other techniques, those illustrated in Figs 64, 65, 66, 67, were adapted to use in the water by the writer. Still other techniques have been modified to eliminate waste motion and to improve mobility. The first edition of this manual, published in 1949, was the first lifesaving and water-safety text to advocate the use of mouth-to-mouth artificial respiration, which has since become widely accepted as the method of first choice.

This manual also should be suitable for use as a text book for high school and college lifesaving courses, particularly in those colleges and universities that offer professional training for Health, Physical Education, and Recreation.

The editorial committee, consisting of Edward L. Griffin, Bernard E. Empleton, Louis A. Cox, and Harold T. Friermood, Chairman, have read all or parts of the manuscript, and to them the writer wishes to express his deepest appreciation. Warm thanks are given also to those men and women whose suggestions over the years have improved the functional use of this manual.

To Drs. Peter V. Karpovich, Arthur H Steinhaus, Robert W. Emery, Kenneth L. McEwen, Walter Greene, Ray T. Smith, Richard R. Scott, Harold Medoff, Harry Memery, and William A. Yorzyk, Jr., the writer is indebted for valuable suggestions concerning the chapter on resuscitation.

Gratitude is expressed to the writer's students of the past twenty-five years, especially to Robert McGrath and Norman Fenn, who co-operated so willing in the first experiments on various procedures and techniques. Thanks are also extended to the writer's graduate assistants for their enthusiastic support.

William Fowler, Fred Lanoue, Harry Baker, Kenneth Chivers, Edward Smyke, and Kenneth Runquist appear with the writer in the photographs, and to them he is extremely grateful. For the competent photography and arduous task of printing the photographs, the writer is indebted to John Mutch and William Pendleton.

Acknowledgment is made to George C. Adams for permission to reproduce several photographs of his ingenious lifesaving devices and the proper use of the resuscitator.

Grateful acknowledgment is extended to Dr. Thomas K. Cureton, Jr., who has made this manual a reality through his stimulating influence and unflagging interest.

To Commander Ellsworth Cook, USNR, since retired, and his associates at the New London Submarine Base, the writer is indebted for valuable information that was incorporated in the section on deep diving.

Acknowledgment is made to the following periodicals, companies, and corporations to which I have referred for material:

The American Journal of Physiology; Archives of Pathology; Beach and Pool; British Medical Journal; Canadian Medical Association Journal; Diving Equipment and Supply Company; Eaton Appliance Corporation; E & J Manufacturing Company; J. E. Emerson Company; P. W. Gallaudet; *Johns Hopkins Hospital Bulletin; Journal of American Medical Association; The Journal of Geology; Journal of Physical Education; Journal of Thoracic Surgery;* Lifetilt Corporation; Lockwood and Company; Los Angeles Department of Playground and Recreation; McKesson Appliance Company: *Research Quarterly;* Sampson Law; Marston and Company; *Scholastic Coach; Science Magazine;* Scott Aviation Corporation; *Statistical Bulletin,* Metropolitan Life Insurance Company; Stephenson Corporation; Stipes Publishing Company; *Surgery; Surgery, Gynecology, and Obstetrics; Swimming Pool Data and Reference Annual; Texas Reports on Biology and Medicine.*

The writer also is appreciative of the permission to use quotations from books published by the following firms:

Appleton-Century-Crofts, New York, N. Y.; Association Press, New York, N. Y.; The Blakiston Co., Philadelphia, Penna.; Boy Scouts of America, New York, N. Y.; Henry Holt & Co., New York, N. Y.; Little Brown & Co., Boston, Mass.; The Macmillan Co., New York, N. Y.; National Safety Council, Chicago, Ill.; Navy Department, Bureau of Ships; Oxford University Press, Inc., New York, N. Y.; Prentice-Hall Inc.,

Englewood Cliffs, N. J.; Reinhold Publishing Corporation, New York, N. Y.; The Riverside Press, Boston, Mass.; W. B. Saunders Company, Philadelphia, Penna.; The Sun Dial Press, New York, N. Y.; John Wiley & Sons, New York, N. Y.; The Williams & Wilkins Company, Baltimore, Md.

Finally, the writer is especially grateful to Dr. Harold T. Friermood for his faith and encouragement during the extended period from the time when this manual was first in the process of development and completion to the present.

CHARLES E. SILVIA

Springfield, Mass.
February, 1965

Contents

1.

Seeking a Perspective on Lifesaving and Water Safety

⁻ AUTHORITIES have estimated that about 110,000,000 people in the United States participate annually in some form of aquatic activity, and this figure is constantly increasing. However, according to Stack and Siebrecht (126),* "of the millions who frequent our beaches each summer, less than 10 per cent swim skillfully." This kind of evidence indicates the tremendous task that confronts all agencies, organizations, and schools to provide education for the people of this country in the techniques of water safety. The amount of progress that has been made toward the goal of water-safety consciousness for the total population is very significant, but we must avoid any tendency to become complacent, because the task of reducing accidental deaths by drowning to the barest minimum is still in its initial stages.

FACTS ABOUT SWIMMING AND DIVING HAZARDS

The death rate (1) from drowning in 1913, the year the safety movement was formally organized, was 10.4 per 100,000 (written as 10.4/100,000) persons or a total of 10,000 deaths. Since 1913, participation in all forms of aquatic activity has increased enormously (1) and if the death rate of 1913

---

* Numbers in parentheses refer to bibliographical sources listed at the end of the book.

had prevailed in 1962, the number of drownings for that year alone would have been increased nearly twofold just on the basis of the population increase. Instead, because of the growth of water-safety consciousness, the death rate has been reduced as low as 3.4/100,000 or 6,400 deaths in 1962; the lowest figure to date. Asphyxia (49) in its various forms has been estimated to claim about 50,000 victims yearly in the United States. The 6,400 deaths caused by submersion asphyxia in 1962 included 3,900 non-swimming fatalities (1) consisting principally of persons "falling into the water from docks, bridges, shores, etc., transport accidents, recreational boating, fishing, ship repair work, and so on, plus accidents in the home and on home premises." Approximately 2,500 drownings were of persons swimming or playing in the water.

The importance of drowning as a cause of death among young people is further emphasized by the fact that, although motor vehicle accidents (1) caused more deaths in 1962 than any other type of accident, among the principal non-motor vehicle type of accident, swimming and non-swimming fatalities were the outstanding type for the young and active ages, which include the age groups of 5–14 years, 15–24 years, and 25–44 years.

Since 1948, drowning and burns have ranked either third or fourth (1) as principal causes of accidental deaths, with motor vehicle accidents first and falls second. For example, in 1948 the death rate for burns was 4.4/100,000 and that of drowning 4.3/100,000, whereas in 1962 the death rate for drowning was 3.4/100,000 and that of burns 4.0/100,000. It is facts such as these that point out the great importance of the need for unremitting preventive efforts on the part of all persons and agencies who recognize the value of human life.

In addition, of the 6,525 deaths caused by drowning in 1961, 5,268, or 85 per cent, were males and 957, or 15 per cent, were females. These facts have interesting implications. Also, approximately 60 per cent of the accidental deaths caused by drowning in 1961 occurred during the months of May, June, July, and August.

An interesting similarity by age groups between drownings and beach rescues is shown in the following chart.

COMPARISON BY AGE GROUPS OF
DROWNINGS AND RESCUES

Age	Drownings (1) 1962	Rank	Rescue (109) 1929–38	Rank
0–4 years	750	5	32	5
5–14 years	1,400	2	833	2
15–24 years	1,450	1	1,000	1
25–44 years	1,300	3	701	3
45–64 years	1,050	4	171	4
65 years and over	450	6	7	6
TOTAL	6,400		2,744	

This chart implies the continued need for water-safety training in schools, camps, and agencies dealing with the school child as well as the importance of swimming under the supervision of properly trained life savers.

The Metropolitan Life Insurance Company (47) reports that at least two hundred deaths are caused yearly in the United States by diving accidents. (This figure may rise unless greater efforts are directed to extension of opportunities for instruction of skin and scuba divers.) This figure is minimal because the deaths of a number of injured divers which are attributed to submersion asphyxia may actually be caused by broken necks, fractured skulls, or other serious injuries. Because diving is a voluntary act, one would suppose that a person who wishes to dive would carefully check to determine the presence of hazards. That this is not the case is shown by an analysis of the records of one hundred policy holders of the Metropolitan Life Insurance Company who were killed in diving accidents. Sixty-eight did not investigate the depth of the water and struck the bottom with sufficient force to cause, in most cases, a broken neck. Eighteen struck submerged objects, such as rocks, and in two cases an oil drum and a tree stump. The remaining fourteen fatalities were caused by such accidents as striking a previous diver, landing flat from a high dive, misjudging distance in diving off a swing, striking a pier, falling on the side of a swimming pool after swinging from the diving board, and diving into the breakers from another person's back. Anyone, regardless of his skill in diving, should adopt a conservative attitude when visiting a pool or beach for the first time. A careful investigation of the water depth and nature of the bottom before diving from any height will result in a sensible course of action.

Small craft, which may be defined as (125) "any watercraft propelled by paddle, oars, or small motor, with a passenger capacity of less than ten," claimed 1,135 drowning victims in 1954. Many well-meaning people who have not mastered the basic swimming and survival skills expose themselves needlessly to the threat of death by drowning. A study (47) by the Minnesota Public Safety Committee showed that 80 per cent of the victims were non-swimmers. An analysis (47) of one hundred policy holders of the Metropolitan Life Insurance Company who were drowned in accidents involving small craft revealed that about two-thirds of the deaths "occurred among persons who were merely cruising or rowing about for pleasure." Accidents involving hunters and fishermen accounted for the remaining third of the deaths. "Rowboats, numerically the preponderant small watercraft, were involved in about half the drownings. Small motorboat mishaps accounted for eighteen deaths; canoes accounted for eighteen; kayaks, four; collapsible canvas boats, four; and sailboats, three."

Tabulation (1) of 2,516 recreational boating deaths reported by the U. S. Coast Guard for 1961-1962 showed 64 per cent to be the fault of the operator.

Cureton and Friermood suggest that the most common causes of water accidents are:

1. Enthusiasm exceeding swimming skill (A little skill is a dangerous thing.)
2. Face-saving, taking dares, showing off (Can't back out now.)
3. Explorer's instinct, raft building, rock hopping, fording streams
4. Unskilled use of small boats, canoes, kayaks, rowboats (They are treacherous.)
5. Muddy and strange waters, sudden drops, holes
6. Hidden underwater dangers: rocks, stumps, mud
7. Disrespect for swift currents, tides, and undertows
8. Underestimation of distance from shore (I thought I could make it.)
9. Sprinting outward, away from shore, too tired on return
10. Swimming and wading alone
11. Artificial supports, water wings, inflated rings
12. Overcrowding boats

OBJECTIVES OF WATER-SAFETY EDUCATION

Every teacher of water safety should have a clear concept of what he hopes to achieve in his teaching. Therefore, he should have in mind several key objectives which will serve to guide his thinking and place his teaching on a high level of effectiveness.

Effective teaching will cause the student to realize the need for:

1. Correct knowledge about the hazards of aquatic participation and how to avoid and prevent accidents
2. Comprehensive training for everyone in swimming and diving information and skills
3. A responsible attitude toward the promotion of safe conduct habits
4. Correct skills in the use of small craft
5. Comprehensive training in lifesaving and water-safety techniques

BRIEF REVIEW OF LIFESAVING TECHNIQUES AND ORGANIZATIONS

Our present knowledge of lifesaving techniques and organizations is enriched by information concerning some of the early practices which reflect man's awareness of his responsibility to society.

1538. Nicholas Winmann (135) wrote the first book on swimming, in which he advocated several practices that are in use today. These practices were: (1) He recognized presence of mind as the most important requisite of the rescuer. (2) The rescuer should not permit the victim to seize him. (3) The rescuer, whenever possible, should have a cord (line) or board with him. (4) The rescuer should be able to swim with only one hand (forerunner of the lifesaving strokes). (5) Disrobing could best be accomplished while treading water.

1555. Olaus Magnus (135) was aware of the need for artificial aids as lifesaving devices for non-swimmers. He also mentioned disrobing.

1767. Society for the Recovery of the Apparently Drowned (21) was founded by a group of community-spirited men in Amsterdam, Holland. The directions of this Society dealt with resuscitative measures. (See Chapter Eleven.)

1774. The Amsterdam Society influenced two English physicians, Dr. Cogan and Dr. Hawes, to bring together a score of leaders in London (Oliver Goldsmith, John Hunter, James Horsfall, and many others) to organize the Royal Humane Society (21). This Society was principally concerned with methods of resuscitation, although it was slow to adopt improved procedures such as were suggested by Dr. Marshall Hall. By 1804 this Society was credited with having saved 2,859 lives. It rewarded 4,587 persons for humane performances. Swimming rescue techniques were not considered within the province of this body, and as late as 1887 (99), when approached by a group interested in teaching swimming, rescue, and resuscitation, the Society did not accept this responsibility. According to Sachs (99), "This lethargy was to some extent overcome in 1882 when, at the suggestion of Dr. Dukes (medical officer of Rugby School), a dummy-saving competition for the public schools, training ships, etc., was instituted. The R.H.S. presented, and still present, a medal to each winner." The Society, in its initial stages, had to overcome many superstitions; one that proved stubborn was the belief that it was unlucky to rescue and revive a drowned person. Finally, in 1782, Dr. Hawes sought legal counsel on this point and was advised that "it was perfectly lawful for any person to assist and to re-

vive another" (21). This superstition survived in a section of Ireland until as late as 1891.

The Society has granted medals for saving life from drowning. "The Stanhope Medal (99), which is awarded to the performer of the most gallant act in any one year, is recognized and valued as the Swimmer's Victoria Cross."

1780. Humane Society of Philadelphia (70) was the first of these organizations in the United States. During the summer months this Society distributed handbills on the dangers of cold water; these were gladly posted by tavern keepers near their doors. Also, it posted signs along the water front telling where its lifesaving apparatus could be found. After a period of inactivity it combined with the Philadelphia Skating Club in 1861.

1786. The Massachusetts Humane Society (70) was patterned after the Royal Humane Society through the influence of Dr. Moyes, who arrived in Boston in 1784. The early methods of resuscitation advocated by this Society were basically the same as those used by the Royal Humane Society. Lifesavers today are not the first to use such lifesaving practices as reaching and wading assists, for on December 13, 1800, the following event took place:

Captain Perkins heard the voice of a female, apparently in distress. Concluding whence the sound came, and calling aloud for help, he ran to the river; throwing off his outside clothes he waded nearly to his chin, and with the help of a stick he reached the then nearest floating person. This was Mr. Card, in the agonies of drowning, who grasped the captain with such violence as both like to have been drowned together. After a severe struggle Captain Perkins recovered himself and forced his way toward the shore, where, by this time, his father had arrived. It was with difficulty, even with the assistance of his father, that Captain Perkins could be disengaged from Mr. Card. The captain's shirt was torn almost entirely off by the grasps of the drowning man. As soon as the captain could be freed he returned after another, while his father, who had waded some distance into the water, with all his clothes on, to expedite the progress of relief, took charge of Mr. Card, dragged him out and laid him on the land. By the time the father had done this, the son had brought another so nigh shore that the father could, by wading to the depth of about three and a half or four feet, take charge also of this other one which he carried and laid on the land. Thus proceeded the son, wading to such depth as to be sometimes buoyed up by the water, bringing human beings back with him and committing them to the care of his father till six persons were collected and placed on the bank. The last that was saved was taken out about fifteen rods below where the canoe was overset. The others were taken out at several intermediate distances. The woman and a child clasped in her arms, were taken up from the bottom of the river where they had sunken to rise no more.

In 1787 the Society erected three huts in Boston Harbor and nearby waters for shelter for shipwrecked sailors. The peak of lifesaving activity was reached in the years 1840-1871, and at one time the Society maintained ninety-two lifesaving stations along the Massachusetts coast. In 1807 the Society constructed the first lifeboat in America at Cohasset, where it remained until 1815.

The Society still carries on several functions, including yearly hiring of several lifeguards for Boston beaches and conducting learn-to-swim campaigns in co-operation with the YMCAs of Massachusetts.

1818. J. Frost (53) was a writer of rare insight, and his descriptions of surface diving, non-swimming and swimming assists, a lifesaving stroke, hair carry, and equipment rescue are noteworthy. Our respect for some of these old writers grows when we read the following passages (53): "It is recommended that one-arm swimming be frequently practised, to qualify for conveying anything out of the water, as well as for lending assistance in case of distress. The writer is of opinion, that a piece of cork fastened to a long slender cord, should be kept in every ferry. This would be found an excellent instrument in case of accident, as it might be cast to the distressed, and when laid hold on would be quickly drawn to land. The cord should be wound round the cork, so as to be in the greatest readiness for use; and should have a knot or two at the end, for good hand-hold."

1867. One of the most remarkable books on swimming was written by Charles Steedman (127). Without the benefit of a vast storehouse of information to draw from, he presented a scholarly treatment of various phases of swimming, including lifesaving. He described surface diving, water wrestling, reaching assist, novice assist, rear approach and hair carry, bobbing rescue, recovery of submerged victim, front head-hold release, disrobing, and the foot block. His description of an unusual rescue follows:

A man fell overboard with a quantity of metal in his pockets. He sank like a stone in water rather turbid, and about fourteen feet deep. As it was dusk when the accident happened, it was absolutely dark at the bottom and impossible to distinguish anything at that depth. His rescuer was guided by the air-bubbles which, escaping from the sunken man's clothing, rose to the surface. Allowing for the set of the current, the swimmer dived right down, and to his surprise was caught in the arms of the drowning man, who hugged him round the neck with his left arm, and buried his right hand in the bushy whiskers of his rescuer. In a position so critical no time was to be lost. The swimmer worked the little finger of the drowning man's hand that was embedded in his beard into his mouth and bit off the tip of it, with, however, but little effect, for the other now clasped his hands round his neck. The swimmer then seized his antagonist, as he now considered him, by the throat with the left hand, and, taking a firm hold of his hair at the back of his head with the other hand, drew his knees up as high as his adversary's chest, and thus tore himself away from the dangerous embrace. Retaining his hold of the other's hair, he brought him to the surface, having been submerged rather more than half a minute, a very considerable time under the circumstances.

1876. R. H. Wallace-Dunlop (143) is the first writer to describe and illustrate "flippers" and may be considered the inventor of these energy-saving devices. In his book he describes the "beaver-tail foot flipper" and the "fishtail foot flipper" and their lifesaving application. These flippers bear a close resemblance to some of the flippers in use today. In recent years we have rediscovered them and they are now widely used for lifesaving, recreational, skin and scuba diving, and underwater demolition purposes.

1890. The U. S. Volunteer Life Saving Corps (59) received articles of incorporation from New York State in 1890. Commodore W. E. Longfellow, who years later contributed so much to the water-safety program of the American Red Cross, acted as General Superintendent with headquarters in New York City. Although there were a number of stations in New York, New Jersey, Pennsylvania, Maryland, Florida, California, Rhode Island, Connecticut, and Massachusetts, the most active groups were in and around New York City. The corps in New York City received an appropriation from the city government which placed it on a more stable operating basis.

The scope of the organization was

to: (1) rescue the drowning, (2) aid the injured, (3) safeguard the public, (4) teach swimming, and (5) reward bravery.

In 1911 the Student Life Saving Corps of YMCA, Springfield College, Springfield, Massachusetts, was organized as an affiliate corps and as one of the student activities.

1891. Largely through the efforts of William Henry and Archibald Sinclair, the Royal Life Saving Society was organized to supplement the work of the Royal Humane Society.

The need that was felt in 1891 was well expressed in the Aims and Objectives of the Society (97):

1. To promote technical education in lifesaving and resuscitation of the apparently drowned.

2. To stimulate public opinion in favor of general adoption of swimming and lifesaving as a branch of instruction in schools, colleges, etc.

3. To encourage floating, diving, plunging, and such other swimming arts as would be of assistance to a person endeavoring to save life.

4. To arrange and promote public lectures, demonstrations and competitions and to form classes of instruction, so as to bring about a widespread and thorough knowledge of the principles which underlie the art of natation.

This organization has exerted strong influence on lifesaving organizations all over the world and at one time its lifesaving techniques were taught in the United States (59). The lifesaving techniques described in the handbook are (97):

(1) approaches—"frontal approach"; (2) releases—"held by the wrists, held by the neck, clutched around the body and arms, clutched around the body from behind"; (3) carries—"when not struggling, when struggling, the arm grip, arms difficult to hold, help when passive, rescue by use of side stroke, 'unigrip' method of

rescue"; (4) recovery from bottom; (5) lifts and carries; (6) Schafer method of artificial respiration.

1907. The Surf Life Saving Association of Australia (5) is one of the foremost surf rescue organizations in the world. In 1902 a small group of enthusiastic surf bathers was responsible for the lifting of the regulations that required segregation of the sexes and limited surf bathing to the early morning hours or late in the day. The increase in the popularity of surf bathing and the parallel increase in drownings led to the organization of several small lifesaving clubs near Sydney. These clubs were composed of volunteers who guarded the beaches during their leisure time. Finally, in 1907, these clubs united to form what was known as the New South Wales Surf Bathing Association and what is today the Surf Life Saving Association of Australia.

From 1907 to the end of the 1937-38 season, over 39,000 rescues have been made by members of this Association. The beaches are patrolled on week ends and holidays from October to April by members of this volunteer organization who must pass a strenuous swimming test and pay subscription fees to gain admission.

1909. The YMCA (35, 36) was the first organization to employ national field representatives to carry out a national educational program of swimming and lifesaving promotion. George Corsan, his son Hebden, and Fred Gallis were employed to teach and promote swimming and lifesaving in the Associations of the United States and Canada. Their work was very successful, and during the years 1909 through 1917 about 376,000 persons were taught swimming and diving. This initial impetus stimulated the growth and development of the YMCA aquatic program to a point never dreamed of by those who pioneered the way. Since 1909, through 1963, a grand total of 18,838,684 persons have been taught to swim (17,184,108) and certified in lifesaving (1,654,576) in the YMCA.

Indoor swimming pool construction received much impetus from the building program of the YMCA. The first "Y" pool (first called a swimming bath), fourteen feet by forty-five feet, was constructed in Brooklyn in 1885. By 1909 there were 293 Associations with swimming pools; today there are nearly 700, and approximately 700 YMCA camps, and the number continues to increase. The tremendous contribution that the YMCA has made to the water-safety consciousness of the American public is a noteworthy example of service to humanity.

In 1913 G. E. Goss completed the first systematic study of lifesaving in the United States as a graduation thesis at Springfield College (60). Later (1916), this work was published by Association Press. The YMCA lifesaver in 1916 was required to (59): "(1) dive into from seven to ten feet of water and bring from bottom to surface a loose bag of sand weighing ten pounds; (2) swim two hundred yards, one hundred on the back without using the hands, and one hundred any other stroke; (3) demonstrate on land five methods of release, in water two methods of release, and the Schafer method of resuscitation; (4) rescue and tow a person of own weight a distance of twenty yards, using two different holds and strokes."

The first formally organized aquatic school was held in Boston in 1916 under the leadership of B. Dean Brink and A. E. Dome. Springfield College, in co-operation with the New England Area Aquatic Committee, conducts an annual four-day aquatic school at Springfield College.

Under the leadership of Dr. Henry F. Kallenberg and Dr. John Brown, Jr., the Aquatic Program prospered until about 1930, when loss of prestige resulted from such factors as inadequately trained leadership, advance of other agency and school programs, insufficient national leadership, and inferior quality of teaching in local Associations. This decline in prestige stimulated the Chicago YMCA Sports Council, under the direction of Robert Hunter and John W. Fuhrer, to propose the revival of a strong national program.

This action culminated in the First National YMCA Aquatic Conference, held in Chicago in 1937. Out of this conference came new leadership (Dr. T. K. Cureton, Jr., Chairman, National YMCA Aquatic Committee) and literature (34, 35, 36) that re-established the program on a high-quality level.

1939-1945. During the period of World War II great emphasis was placed upon aquatic survival techniques and warfare aquatics. Cureton's nation-wide instructional clinics and his book (32) dealing with these matters made a noteworthy contribution to aquatics. It was during the war period that scuba diving made significant advances that were to stimulate civilian interest soon thereafter.

1951. The Council for National Cooperation in Aquatics (CNCA), following six years of preliminary work, was formed in October 1951. This brought together some 25 national organizations for joint sharing, planning, and promotion of aquatics. Dr. Robert J. H. Kiphuth of Yale University and Dr. Harold T. Friermood of the National Board of YMCAs are credited with being the organizers and served as the first and second respective elected chairmen.

The Second National YMCA Aquatic Conference, held near Chicago in 1949, re-evaluated the Aquatic Program in the light of the past twelve years' experience.

The Third National Aquatic Conference was held in 1954 at Michigan State University, East Lansing, Michigan, and served to provide renewed impetus to the Aquatic Program through the combined efforts of the outstanding leaders in the field of aquatics.

In 1957 the CNCA-sponsored book, edited by Bernard E. Empleton, *Science of Skin and Scuba Diving*, was widely received and after several reprintings was revised and issued as *The New Science of Skin and Scuba Diving*. (45). It was approved for listing in the YMCA Aquatic Literature—Professional Series.

Early in 1958, the *New YMCA Aquatic Workbook* (52) edited by Dr. Harold T. Friermood was published as a volume in the YMCA Aquatic Literature—Professional Series. This brought together in one book a dozen major units of the broad YMCA aquatic program.

The Fourth National YMCA Aquatic Conference was held at George Williams College, Chicago, August 23-30, 1959.

The day following the conference was spent by Bernard E. Empleton and his committee in testing and certifying approximately 25 instructors for YMCA leadership in skin and scuba diving. This was the first National YMCA Certifying Institute to put into practice the newly developed program and standards approved during the conference.

The Fifth National YMCA Aquatic Conference was held May 17–21, 1964, at George Williams College Camp on Lake Geneva, Wisconsin. Six major areas were studied in depth, and recommendations were acted upon by the entire conference body assembled in plenary sessions. Later the more than 60 recommendations were presented to the National YMCA Physical Education Committee for approval. Renewal was called for in YMCA Lifesaving certification annually; Leader-Examiners to be certified every two years; Aquatic Instructors every three years; and Aquatic

Directors every five years. YMCA Lifesaving certification was specified as a requirement for becoming a YMCA Scuba Leader-Examiner or Scuba Instructor. A number of changes in procedures were instituted, including the appointment of Area/State Scuba Commissioners and the authorization of a number of important publications.

The First (52) Conference for National Cooperation in Aquatics, changed in 1964 and legally incorporated as Council for National Cooperation in Aquatics (CNCA), was held at Yale University in October 1951 with the YMCA playing a key role in formulating pre-conference plans and procedures. The next nine were also held at Yale. The Eleventh and Twelfth Conferences were held at Indiana University. The Thirteenth Conference was held in November of 1964 at the University of Georgia. The YMCA has continued to provide leadership and strong faith in this important project.

The prime objective of the YMCA Aquatic Program is: *Teach America to Swim,* and encourage every swimmer to become a lifesaver.

1914. The American Red Cross (36, 58), through its lifesaving and water-safety program, has stimulated widespread interest in the need for adequate aquatic leadership, protection, and prevention throughout the United States. This organization has made a great contribution to reducing the number of yearly drownings by its instructional program in swimming, lifesaving, and small craft operation. Through the leadership and publications of such men as Commodore W. E. Longfellow, who was the first national field representative and later directed the work of the staff of National Field Representatives, and Carroll L. Bryant, who served as the national director of the Water Safety Service, this organization exerts a strong influence on the aquatic thinking of the American people. Richard L. Brown succeeded Carroll L. Bryant in 1951 and gave his leadership to this organization until his death in May of 1964. The Red Cross continues to exert a strong influence on the aquatic thinking of the American people through the guidance of Alfred W. Cantrell, National Director, Safety Services, and E. J. Mongeon, National Director, Water Safety.

In 1909 the American Red Cross and the YMCA entered into an agreement to promote first aid on a national basis and give joint certificates for standardized first-aid courses. This arrangement resulted in frequent conferences, and during one of these conferences the question was asked whether the Red Cross had considered the desirability of promoting instruction in lifesaving as part of the first-aid training. This question was seriously considered, and at a later meeting between representatives of the two organizations the Red Cross signified that if the proper leadership could be secured they would begin such a program. Commodore W. E. Longfellow was recommended for the position, and his effective promotional efforts have left a lasting imprint.

A comparison of the comprehensive standards of the present-day program of the American Red Cross and the requirements for certification in 1916 is clearly indicative of progress (59).

1. Beginners must be able to swim fifty feet, using any stroke they prefer.
2. Swimmers must be able to swim one hundred yards, using two or more strokes; to dive properly from a take-off; to swim on back fifty feet; and to retrieve objects at reasonable depths from the surface.
3. Lifesavers must be able to tow a person of their own weight ten yards by each of the following methods: (a) head carry, using two hands and swimming on back; (b) under-arm carry, using two hands and swimming on back; (c) across-chest carry, using one arm and side stroke; (d) using

breast stroke, hands of rescued on shoulders.

They must be able to show in the water three methods of releasing themselves from people in peril of drowning when grasped by: (a) wrist hold, (b) front neck hold, (c) back neck hold.

They are required to demonstrate both the Schafer and Silvester methods of performing artificial respiration, although the Schafer method is the one preferred.

1924. The campaign (17), "Every Scout a Swimmer," was started by Dr. James E. West, the Chief Scout Executive, in 1924. The first edition of the Boy Scout book, *Swimming, Water Sports, and Safety*, was assembled by Commodore W. E. Longfellow in the same year. This book and the succeeding editions have contributed to the fund of aquatic knowledge, and the success of the program is reflected by the thousands of Scouts who have been taught swimming, lifesaving, accident prevention, and small craft handling.

Fred C. Mills, who was national director of Health and Safety, and the present director Donald Higgins and his associate E. E. Hoisington have added to the prestige of the program by providing the aquatic merit badge series of publications. No student, aquatic leader, or teacher can afford to by-pass the wealth of information found in the publications of the Boy Scouts of America.

1935. The National Collegiate Life Saving Society was organized by the College Swimming Coaches Association in 1935. At that time a majority of the swimming coaches felt there was a need for a distinctive collegiate lifesaving society. The standards were published in the Collegiate Swimming Guide for several years. However, in 1941 the Society was voted out of existence.

1936. Fred R. Lanoue started his revolutionary survival concept at the Atlanta Athletic Club, and his work at Georgia Tech has earned him world-wide acclaim. His book entitled *Drownproofing* (83) has received wide approval by water-safety experts.

1960. Dr. Richard H. Pohndorf completed his book *Camp Waterfront Programs and Management* (94), an expansion of an earlier work in 1946, that dealt with important aspects of water safety.

Following this brief historical perspective on Aquatics as it relates to lifesaving and water safety, the reader's attention is now directed to—Lifesaving and Water Safety Skill Categories. This involves:

The judgment and perspective of the aquatic student, leader, and teacher will be enhanced when the following major categories of lifesaving, water safety, and watermanship skills are kept in mind: (1) lifesaving prerequisites, (2) personal safety skills, (3) non-swimming assists, (4) swimming assists, (5) approaches and tows, (6) body recovery, (7) defensive tactics, (8) releases, (9) water wrestling, (10) equipment rescue, (11) lifts, carries, and let-downs, (12) resuscitation.

2.

How to Teach Lifesaving and Water Safety

THE phrase, "lifesaving through watermanship," states the concept of the type of lifesaving course taught in this book. The lifesaver who has successfully completed a lifesaving course that emphasizes water agility, breath control (including exclusion of water from nose, breath holding, and organic condition), emotional fitness, and an intelligent aggressive attitude is well equipped to cope with a wide variety of rescue situations. The instructor should constantly bear in mind the significance of providing a directed experience that will remain with the lifesaver long after he has forgotten the details of some technique. Techniques are important but not nearly so important as the fundamentals of watermanship.

This course requires a maximum expression of skill and emotional fitness, and not every student will possess or acquire these attributes to the degree necessary to complete successfully the requirements on the first try. The student, however, who has progressed through the YMCA swimming and diving program should find this course to be an additional challenge to his physical and emotional capacities.

The course outline for junior and senior and YMCA lifesavers which follows in this chapter consists of twenty-two one-hour lesson plans that are designed to prepare the student for the maximum effort that is necessary for the final practical examination. For the junior course the instructor may reduce

by half the support, approach, and tow distances.

No time allotment is made in the lesson plans for demonstration and explanation because this aspect of the course will vary according to the ability of the instructor to present the material concisely but lucidly. Visual aids in the form of moving pictures, film strips, and demonstrations should be scheduled to motivate the student and increase his over-all perspective. The instructor should be constantly striving to awaken the curiosity of his students and provide them with a lasting emotional and cerebral experience. Land drills should be used only when absolutely necessary. Generally speaking, the time consumed by land drills can be used to a greater advantage in water drill.

Cureton (29) offers some valuable teaching hints for student and instructor:

1. The more recent the practice, the more perfect will be its reproduction.

2. The individual tends to repeat that which is satisfying and to avoid that which is annoying.

3. Poor organization which results in delay may cause some dissatisfaction.

4. Attention is desired but not under rigid compulsion.

5. Failure is unpleasant and although there will be some failure in every lesson there must be also some definite accomplishment.

6. Patience, perseverance, tact, and enthusiasm are prime requisites for a successful teacher.

7. Best results will be obtained when

the periods are of such length as to be the most economical to the individual.

8. Repetition is a necessary factor in the learning process.

9. The reactions of the learners should be carefully watched and they should be favored as far as may be reasonable.

10. Adequate technical training is im-

perative. It is necessary to know in practice as well as in theory.

11. The science of teaching centers largely around exact knowledge of the skills to be taught and the mechanics of their execution.

12. Disagreeable conditions are to be avoided.

LIFESAVING AND WATER-SAFETY COURSE OUTLINE

FIRST CLASS

(20 min.)   *Introductory Remarks*

1. HEALTH AND SANITATION
   a. Toilet and shower procedure
   b. Caution against wearing footwear on pool deck
   c. Control of expectoration
   d. Importance of breath control
   e. Caution against swimming while enduring a cold

2. SAFETY PRECAUTIONS
   a. Do not bound on the diving board
   b. Know water depths
   c. Do not dive until way is clear
   d. Do not swim in diving area
   e. Do not run; do not push or duck another swimmer
   f. Keep fingernails trimmed

3. ATTENDANCE
   a. 100 per cent attendance expected
   b. Attend class even though a non-participant

4. CERTIFICATION
   a. YMCA junior or senior lifesaver

5. COURSE OBJECTIVES
   a. To develop skill, endurance, and confidence in the execution of life-saving and water safety skills to the highest level of efficiency possible
   b. To understand the key principles which are basic to the efficient execution of lifesaving and water skills
   c. To develop watermanship which consists of water agility, breath control, controlled combativeness, and emotional readiness to a high degree

Review: Prerequisites and personal safety

(6 min.)   1. HYPERVENTILATION (10 times), cross-pool plunge and glide, correct turn, underwater push and glide on front, underwater push and glide on back, correct turn, underwater push and glide. Repeat as often as time will permit.
   a. Review breath-holding and exclusion of water from the nose while on the back
   b. See Figs. 1a, 1b, 2a, 2b, 2c

(10 min.)   2. STROKES

     a. Clockwise continuous swim around pool, slower swimmers on the outside, faster swimmers on the inside

     b. Underarm side stroke (both sides), overarm side stroke, breast stroke, elementary back stroke, legs alone on back, lifesaving stroke (both sides), crawl stroke (1 minute each stroke)

     c. See Figs. 3a, 3b, 3c, 4, 5a, 5b, 6, 7a, 7b, 8a, 8b, 8c, 8d, 9a, 9b, 9c, 10a, 10b

(3 min.)   3. BOBBING

     a. Whole class at deep water end. Emphasize steady continuous exhalation through the nostrils for four seconds during descent and ascent

     b. See Figs. 17a, 17b. Note that the technique used for the feet-first surface dive is identical to that used for bobbing

(3 min.)   4. VERTICAL SUPPORT

     a. Class remains at deep water end

       1) 1 minute, legs alone. See Figs. 13a, 13b, 14a, 14b

       2) 2 minutes, whole stroke. See Fig. 12

(5 min.)   5. SURVIVAL POSITIONS

     a. See Figs. 11, 11a, 11b

     b. On command, "Survival on front (or back)," class assumes position given

     c. On command, "Float," class stops supporting action with legs and attempts to float. See Figs. 15a, 15b

(6 min.)   6. SURFACE DIVING

     a. Class at deep end

     b. Head first and feet first, surface dives, remain underwater 10 seconds each time

       1) 4 repetitions of each as though conducting an underwater search

       2) See Figs. 16a, 16b, 17a, 17b

(7 min.)   7. UNDERWATER SWIMMING

     a. Class counts off by fours

     b. Standard procedure, plunge entry, swim 1 length under water, return to starting position. Repeat as many times as possible. Emphasize hyperventilation. See Figs. 9a, 9b, 9c

     c. Standard procedure

       1) When the plunge entry is used each swimmer should wait until the swimmer that precedes him in his lane has covered 25 feet before leaving the mark. This distance is reduced to 10 feet when the feet-first entry is used

       2) Lesson plan items 2, 3, 4, 5, and 6, under Review are continuous

SECOND CLASS

Review: Prerequisites and personal safety

(4 min.)   1. HYPERVENTILATION, cross-pool plunge and glide, correct turn, underwater push and glide on front, underwater push and glide on back, correct turn, underwater push and glide. Repeat as often as time will permit

(10 min.)   2. STROKES

     a. Clockwise continuous swim around pool. Slower swimmers on the outside, faster swimmers on the inside

     b. Underarm side stroke (both sides), overarm side stroke, breast stroke, elementary back stroke, legs alone on back, lifesaving stroke (both sides), crawl stroke (1 minute each stroke)

(3 min.)   3. BOBBING

(2 min.)   4. VERTICAL SUPPORT
           Note: Legs alone

(3 min.)   5. SURFACE DIVING
           Note: Head first from vertical position

(5 min.)   6. SURVIVAL POSITIONS
           a. See Figs. 11, 11a, 11b
           b. On command, "Survival on front (or back)," class assumes position given
           c. On command, "Float," class stops supporting action with legs and attempts to float. See Figs. 15a, 15b

(8 min.)   7. UNDERWATER SWIMMING
           a. Class counts off by fours
           b. Standard procedure, plunge entry, swim 1 length under water, return to starting position. Repeat as many times as possible. Emphasize proper use of hyperventilation

New: Personal safety

(10 min.)   1. CRAMP TREATMENT
           a. See Figs. 25a, 25b

(15 min.)   2. DISROBING AND USE OF TROUSERS AND SHIRT AS SUPPORTS
           a. Emphasize importance of using trousers and shirt as supports. See Figs. 26a, 26b, 26c, 26d, 27a, 27b, 27c, 27d, 27e, 27f, 28a, 28b
           b. Lesson plan items 2, 3, 4, 5, and 6 under Review are continuous

THIRD CLASS

Review: Prerequisites and personal safety

(35 min.)   1. REPEAT LESSON PLAN ITEMS 1, 2, 3, 4, 5, and 6, under Review in Second Class

(15 min.)   2. DISROBING AND USE OF TROUSERS AND SHIRT AS SUPPORTS

(10 min.)   *New:* Prerequisites and personal safety
           1. USE OF OTHER SUPPORTS. See Fig. 29
           Note: Trap air in pail, number ten can, bag, pillow case, jug, canteens, etc.
           2. LASH SEVERAL OARS, PADDLES, OR PIECES OF WOOD TOGETHER

FOURTH CLASS

(35 min.)   *Review:* Prerequisites and personal safety
           Note: REPEAT LESSON PLAN ITEMS 1, 2, 3, 4, 5, and 6, under Review in Second Class

(25 min.)   *New:* RECOVERY OF SUBMERGED VICTIM
           1. By two's, simulate search of bottom of pool, starting at one side at deep end and swimming back and forth across pool, progressing gradually into shallow water. Repeat feet-first surface dives as needed. Standard procedure, stride jump entry. See Chapter Four and Figs. 18, 19, 20a, 20b, 21a, 21b, 22, 23, 24, 39a
           2. Introduce the use of the face mask, flippers, snorkle, and scuba.

FIFTH CLASS

Review: Prerequisites and personal safety

(30 min.)   NOTE: REPEAT LESSON PLAN ITEMS 1, 2, 3, 4, and 5, under Review in Second Class

New

(15 min.)   1. NON-SWIMMING ASSISTS
a. Reaching and wading assists
Note: Count off by two's and spread out along sides of pool
b. See Figs. 30a, 30b, 30c, 30d, 30e, 31a, 31b

(15 min.)   2. SWIMMING ASSISTS
Stride-jump entry assist, 30 feet each, rescuer and victim change, standard procedure. See Fig. 39a
a. Novice assists
1) On front. See Fig. 34
2) On back. See Fig 35
b. Arm Assist. See Fig. 36

SIXTH CLASS

Review: Prerequisites and personal safety

(4 min.)   1. HYPERVENTILATION, cross-pool plunge and glide, correct turn, underwater push and glide on front, underwater push and glide on back, correct turn, underwater push and glide. Repeat as often as time will permit.

(2 min.)   2. VERTICAL SUPPORT
Note: Legs alone

(4 min.)   3. BOBBING
Note: 10-20 seconds breath-holding on bottom

(4 min.)   4. SURVIVAL POSITIONS

New: Swimming assists

(15 min.)   1. CLOTHING ASSISTS
By partners at the deep end. Repeat as many times as possible
a. Supporting tired swimmer. See Fig. 32
b. Supporting exhausted swimmer and inflating trousers. See Figs. 33a, 33b, 33c, 33d

(5 min.)   2. SHOULDER WRESTLING. See Fig. 37
a. By partners at deep end
b. Emphasize superiority of horizontal position over vertical position

(16 min.)   3. TIRED SWIMMER ASSIST
a. On starting signal from instructor, rescuers execute correct approach procedure and swim continuously with victim for two minutes around pool. Repeat alternately four times
b. Emphasize that rescuer should make contact with some forward motion in a horizontal swimming position. Also, rescuer should give commands in a loud, clear voice. See Figs. 38a, 38b, 38c, 38d, 38e

(10 min.)   4. DEFENSE AGAINST PANICKY, TIRED SWIMMER
a. Stride-jump entry, tow 60 feet, execute 360-degree turn halfway, standard procedure
b. Emphasize that rescuer should anticipate the possibility of the victim attempting to grasp him. See Fig. 39

SEVENTH CLASS

Review:

(14 min.)   1. PREREQUISITES AND PERSONAL SAFETY
Note: Repeat lesson plan items 1, 2, 3, and 4, under Review in Sixth Class

(10 min.)   2. SWIMMING ASSISTS
a. Clothing assists
Note: By pairs at deep end. Repeat as many times as possible

(10 min.)   b. Tired swimmer assist
Note: On starting signal from instructor, rescuers execute correct approach procedure and swim continuously with victim for five minutes around pool.

New: Approaches and tows

1. APPROACH STROKING AND REVERSE
a. Emphasize looking at victim during approach swim, tight tuck and vigorous forward sweeping action with arms during reverse prior to making contact with victim. See Figs. 40-41
b. With whole class in water execute the following approaches and tows

(16 min.)   2. REAR ARMPIT APPROACH AND CROSS-CHEST TOW
a. Emphasize that the rescuer should grasp the victim's armpit in such a manner that his fingers extend in front of it and his thumb behind it. Also, vigorous stroking movements should be used to get under way. See Figs. 42a, 42b
b. Emphasize that the rescuer should maintain a snug, firm grip during the cross-chest tow. See Fig. 48. Tow victim continuously for two minutes around pool. Repeat alternately four times

(10 min.)   3. FRONT UPPER-ARM APPROACH AND ARMPIT TOW
a. Emphasize that the rescuer should employ vigorous stroking movements to get under way. See Figs. 44a, 44b, 53

EIGHTH CLASS

Review

(14 min.)   1. PREREQUISITES AND PERSONAL SAFETY
Note: Repeat lesson plan items 1, 2, 3, and 4, under Review in Sixth Class

(10 min.)   2. APPROACHES AND TOWS
a. Rear armpit approach and cross-chest tow
Note: Repeat same practice procedure used in Seventh Class

(10 min.)   b. Front upper-arm approach and armpit tow

New: Approaches and tows

(10 min.)   1. COMPACT JUMP
Note: Use diving board when greater heights are not available. See Fig. 39b

(8 min.)   2. REAR CHIN APPROACH AND HEAD TOW
a. Repeat same practice procedure used in Seventh Class
b. Emphasize correct chin grasp and towing position. See Figs. 43-51

(8 min.)   3. FRONT WRIST APPROACH AND HAIR TOW
Note: Emphasize correct hair hold and control of towing arm. See Figs. 45a, 45b, 50

NINTH CLASS

Review

(14 min.)   1. PREREQUISITES AND PERSONAL SAFETY

Note: Repeat lesson plan items 1, 2, 3, and 4, under Review in Sixth Class

(24 min.)   2. APPROACHES AND TOWS

With whole class in water execute the following approaches and tow the victim continuously for three minutes around the pool. Repeat alternately for each procedure

    a. Rear armpit approach and cross-chest tow
    b. Rear chin approach and head tow
    c. Front upper-arm approach and armpit tow
    d. Front wrist approach and hair tow

New: Approaches and tows

(12 min.)   1. FRONT UNDERWATER APPROACH AND CONTROL TOW

    a. Emphasize control of victim. See Figs. 46, 47a, 47b, 49
    b. With whole class in water execute approach and tow the victim continuously for one minute. Repeat alternately four times

(10 min.)   2. APPROACH AND TOW 2 PERSONS

    a. Count off by threes, stride-jump entry, approach swim 15 feet, tow 20 feet. See Fig. 54

TENTH CLASS

Review

(14 min.)   1. PREREQUISITES AND PERSONAL SAFETY

    a. Repeat lesson plan items 1, 2, 3, and 4, under Review in Sixth Class

(10 min.)   2. SWIMMING ASSISTS

    a. Tired swimmer support, clockwise around pool for 5 minutes. This exercise is continuous from horizontal stationary support

(24 min.)   3. APPROACHES AND TOWS

    a. Rear armpit approach and cross-chest tow
Stride-jump entry, approach swim 60 yds., tow 60 yds., clockwise around pool. At end of tow, control vigorously struggling partner

(12 min.)   *New:* Defensive tactics

Partners on opposite sides of pool, execute technique in center of pool

    1. TWO-HAND BLOCK AND FOOT BLOCK

    a. Emphasize vigorous action by both partners. Avoid kicking partner. See Figs. 55a, 55b, 55c, 55d

ELEVENTH CLASS

Review

    1. PREREQUISITES

(4 min.)   a. Hyperventilation (10 times), cross-pool plunge and glide, correct turn, underwater push and glide on front, underwater push and glide on back, correct turn, underwater push and glide. Repeat as often as time will permit

(2 min.)   b. Vertical support
Note: Legs alone

(4 min.)   c. Bobbing
Note: 10-20 seconds breath-holding on bottom

(10 min.)   2. SWIMMING ASSISTS
a. Tired swimmer support, clockwise around pool for 5 minutes

(28 min.)   3. APPROACHES AND TOWS
a. Front upper arm approach and armpit tow
Stride-jump entry, approach swim 80 yds., tow 80 yds., clockwise around pool. At end of tow, control vigorously struggling partner

(12 min.)   4. DEFENSIVE TACTICS
a. Two-hand block and foot block
Repeat procedure used in Tenth Class

TWELFTH CLASS

Review

(10 min.)   1. PREREQUISITES
a. Repeat lesson plan items 1, 2, and 3, under Review in Eleventh Class

(10 min.)   2. SWIMMING ASSISTS
a. See Eleventh Class, item 2

3. APPROACHES AND TOWS
(8 min.)   a. Rear chin approach and head tow
With whole class in water execute approach and tow the victim continuously for two minutes. Repeat alternately twice
(6 min.)   b. Front wrist approach and hair tow

Note: Repeat same procedure used in "a"

(6 min.)   4. DEFENSIVE TACTICS
Note: Two-hand block and foot block

New: Defensive tactics
Partners on opposite sides of pool, execute technique 8 feet from victim's side of pool

(12 min.)   1. REAR PIVOT BREAKAWAY
a. Emphasize quick downward rotating action of head followed by vigorous push. See Figs. 56a, 56b
Note: Drill on this movement by instructing class to snap pivot on command "Turn." Repeat 6 times before trying complete technique
b. After 2 practice efforts the victim should make maximum effort to grasp rescuer. Repeat as many times as time permits

(8 min.)   2. FRONT PARRY
a. Emphasize point that this technique is used only when victim is very close to rescuer and moving toward him. See Figs. 57a, 57b. Repeat as many times as time permits.

THIRTEENTH CLASS

Review

(10 min.)   1. PREREQUISITES
a. Repeat lesson plan items 1, 2, and 3, under Review in Eleventh Class

(30 min.)   2. SWIMMING ASSISTS, APPROACHES, AND TOWS
a. Stride-jump entry, approach swim 60 yds., recover partner from bottom at deep end of pool, water 12 feet deep for juniors, 16 feet deep for

seniors, when conditions permit; cross-chest tow 60 yds., armpit tow 60 yds., tired swimmer support for 5 minutes

Remember swim clockwise around pool, slow traffic outside, fast traffic inside

(20 min.)   3. DEFENSIVE TACTICS
Repeat as many times as time permits
a. Two-hand block and foot block
b. Rear pivot breakaway
c. Front parry

FOURTEENTH CLASS

Review

(10 min.)   1. PREREQUISITES
a. Repeat lesson plan items 1, 2, and 3, under Review in Eleventh Class

(20 min.)   2. SWIMMING ASSISTS, APPROACHES, AND TOWS
a. Stride-jump entry, approach swim 20 yds., recover partner from bottom at deep end of pool, cross-chest tow 20 yds., hair tow 20 yds., head tow 20 yds., tired swimmer support for 3 minutes
Clockwise pool procedure

(10 min.)   3. DEFENSIVE TACTICS
Repeat as many times as time permits
a. Two-hand block and foot block
b. Rear pivot breakaway
c. Front parry

New: Releases
Partners on opposite sides of pool, execute technique 8 feet from victim's side of pool. Repeat as many times as time permits

(8 min.)   1. DOUBLE GRIP ON ONE ARM RELEASE
a. Emphasize vigorous maximum efforts by both partners. Don't forget control position. See Figs. 58a, 58b

(12 min.)   2. FRONT HEAD HOLD AND BODY SCISSORS RELEASE
a. Confidence support 1 minute, then front head hold and body scissors assist 15 yds., and then release. See Figs. 59a, 59b, 59c, 59d, 60
Emphasize importance of staying on same plane as victim, horizontal position, and supporting leg action during head-hold release. Grasp victim by the hair when long enough, to increase discomfort and leverage

FIFTEENTH CLASS

Review

(10 min.)   1. PREREQUISITES
a. Repeat lesson plan items 1, 2, and 3, under Review in Eleventh Class

(16 min.)   2. RELEASES
Repeat as many times as time permits
a. Double grip on one arm release
b. Front head hold and body scissors release

New: Releases
Same practice procedure. Repeat as many times as time permits

(8 min.)   1. FRONT HEAD HOLD RELEASE (push away)
a. Emphasize importance of placing forehead on top of victim's collar bone (clavicle) to avoid under-arm strangle. See Figs. 61-64

(8 min.)   2. REAR PIVOT RELEASE
            a. Emphasize importance of rotating head rather than ducking head.
            See Figs. 62a, 62b, 62c, 62d

(8 min.)   3. HEAD LOCK SOMERSAULT RELEASE
            a. Grasp victim by the hair when long enough to increase discomfort
            and leverage. See Fig. 62c

(10 min.)   4. ASSISTING WOULD-BE RESCUER
            Count off by threes, repeat until each lifesaver acts as rescuer. See Fig. 63

SIXTEENTH CLASS

Review

            1. PREREQUISITES
(2 min.)   a. Vertical support
            Note: Legs alone

(4 min.)   b. BOBBING
            Note: 10-20 seconds breath-holding on bottom

(30 min.)   2. COMBINATION SERIES
            a. Stride-jump entry, approach swim 40 yds., feet-first surface dive, re-
            cover partner from bottom at deep end of pool, cross-chest tow 40 yds.,
            armpit tow 40 yds., tired swimmer assist 5 minutes, front head hold and
            body scissors release, rear pivot breakaway or release, control tow to side
            of pool or dock

(24 min.)   3. RELEASES
            a. Double grip on one arm release
            b. Rear pivot release
            c. Headlock somersault release

SEVENTEENTH CLASS

New

(25 min.)   1. WATER WRESTLING
            a. Practice of pinning holds. Emphasize importance of observing pre
            cautionary measures
            1) Underarm strangle. See Fig. 64
            2) Control carry with or without body scissors. See Fig. 65
            3) Judo strangle. See Fig. 66
            4) Double stretch. See Fig. 67
               (a) Also, neck strangle

(20 min.)   b. Competition
            Note: Total of 2 matches for each lifesaver
            Winners meet winners, losers meet losers

(15 min.)   2. LIFTS, CARRIES, AND LET-DOWNS
            a. Pool lift
            Emphasize importance of correct lifting technique. See Figs. 77a, 77b
            77c, 77d

EIGHTEENTH CLASS

(60 min.)   *Final practical examination for Senior Lifesaver Certification*
            1. INSTRUCTIONS
            Note: Test items are to be performed continuously from start to finish
            No rest stops are permitted for certification. Use clockwise pool pro
            cedure.

    2. TEST ITEMS
      a. Jog (run when conditions permit) 100 yds.
      b. Approach swim 100 yds. (60 yds. crawl, 40 yds. optional strokes, excluding back strokes)
      c. Feet-first surface dive, recover partner from bottom of pool at deep end
      d. Tow 100 yds. (40 yds. cross-chest tow, 60 yds. optional tows, except tired swimmer assist)
      e. Tired swimmer assist for 5 minutes
      f. Release front head hold and body scissors
      g. Rear pivot breakaway or rear pivot release
      h. Control tow to side of pool
      i. Pool lift
      j. Start artificial respiration

(45 min.) *Final practical examination for Junior Lifesaver Certification*
    1. INSTRUCTIONS
    Note: Test items must be performed continuously from start to finish. No rest stops are permitted for certification

    2. TEST ITEMS
      a. Jog (run when conditions permit) 50 yds.
      b. Approach swim 60 yds. (30 yds. crawl, 30 yds. optional strokes, excluding back strokes)
      c. Feet-first surface dive, recover partner from bottom of pool at deep end
      d. Tow 60 yds. (20 yds. cross-chest tow, 40 yds. optional tows, except tired swimmer assist)
      e. Tired swimmer assist for 3 minutes
      f. Release front head hold and body scissors
      g. Rear pivot breakaway or rear pivot release
      h. Control tow to side of pool
      i. Pool lift
      j. Start artificial respiration

NINETEENTH CLASS
New

(40 min.) 1. EQUIPMENT RESCUE
    Count off by threes, repeat until each lifesaver acts as rescuer
    a. Shoulder loop and line. See Figs. 68a, 68b, 68c, 69
    b. Ring buoy. See Fig. 70
    c. Torpedo buoy. See Figs. 71a, 71b, 71c, 71d, 72a, 72b
    d. Heaving line. See Fig. 73
    e. Discussion and/or demonstration
      1) Surfboard. See Figs. 74a, 74b, 74c, 75a, 75b
      2) Life boat. See Figs. 76a, 76b

(20 min.) 2. LIFTS, CARRIES, AND LET-DOWNS
    Shallow water practice
    a. One-man drag. See Figs. 82a, 82b, 82c
    b. Fireman's carry. See Figs. 78a, 78b, 78c
    c. Saddle-back carry. See Figs. 80a, 80b, 80c

TWENTIETH CLASS

The next three classes can be conducted more effectively in the gymnasium and class room

(30 min.)   *Review:* Lifts, carries, and let-downs
1. FIREMEN'S CARRY AND LET-DOWN. See Figs. 79a, 79b, 79c
2. SADDLE-BACK CARRY AND LET-DOWN. See Figs. 80a, 80b, 80c, 81a, 81b
3. ONE-MAN DRAG. See Figs. 82a, 82b, 82c
4. TWO-MAN CARRY. See Fig. 83
5. THREE-MAN CARRY
6. STRADDLE-BACK CARRY
7. SUPPORTING CARRY

(30 min.)   *New:* Methods of artificial respiration
1. NIELSEN METHOD. See Figs. 84a, 84b, 84c 85a, 85b
2. BACK PRESSURE—HIP ROLL METHOD. See Figs. 86a, 86b, 87a, 87b
3. BACK PRESSURE—HIP LIFT METHOD. See Figs. 86a, 86b, 86c
4. SILVESTER METHOD. See page 135.
5. MODIFIED MANUAL ARTIFICIAL RESPIRATION METHODS. See Fig. 92
6. EXPIRED AIR METHODS. See Figs. 88a, 88b, 89, 90
7. CLOSED-CHEST (EXTERNAL) CARDIAC MASSAGE. See Fig. 91.

TWENTY-FIRST CLASS

Review

(20 min.)   1. METHODS OF ARTIFICIAL RESPIRATION
            a. See Twentieth Class

(40 min.)   2. MECHANICAL METHODS OF ARTIFICIAL RESPIRATION
            a. Arrange for demonstration of resuscitation and inhalator by fire or police department or representative of manufacturer
            Note: See Figs. 93a, 93b, 93c, 93d, 93e, 94

TWENTY-SECOND CLASS

(20 min.)   *Final examination on artificial respiration:* Combine land carry, let-down, and expired air methods
1. *Emphasize importance of not wasting precious seconds*
2. *Perform expired air methods at 2-minute intervals for 10 minutes*

(40 min.)   *Theoretical examination for Junior or Senior Lifesaver Certification*
1. *Passing grade for Juniors under 15 years of age—60*
2. *Passing grade for Seniors 15 years of age and above—75*

3.

Prerequisites

Introduction. The writer has felt it wise to include in this work a group of prerequisite skills that are related to lifesaving and water safety. In the selection of these seventeen skills, the work done by Cureton (34) on the intermediate swimming level has served as a guide.

"Prerequisite" may be defined as something necessary to produce a desired result. The desired result we are seeking is complete mastery of the YMCA lifesaving skills. The prospective lifesaver must be aware that he cannot attain proficiency as a lifesaver unless he is well versed in these prerequisite or fundamental skills. Although these basic skills may be reviewed during the lifesaving course, the process of learning them must have taken place before the course is undertaken.

Fig. 1a. Starting position

Plunge. Conscious body control from fingers to toes provides a streamlined entry into the water that conserves the swimmer's energy by carrying him a maximum distance under water without stroking.

The feet are directly under the hips about eight inches apart, knees flexed slightly, trunk flexed horizontally, arms hanging vertically, head up, and eyes fixed on a point on the water about twelve feet away.

Fig. 1b.   Flight

The position in flight is the result of properly timed action of the arms and legs. The arms are swung backward to start the body moving forward and then swung forward vigorously to the position of extreme flexion overhead. The extension of hips, knees, and ankles, if started too soon, will result in an upward rather than outward movement of the body, which will cause the head to be higher than the legs during the flight. A head-first entry is then made possible only by flexing the trunk (jack-knife position). Note the absence of an arch, the fully extended position of the knees, ankles, and elbows, and the flexed position of the toes.

Push and Glide. Although this skill is used principally in a closed course as an important part of a turn, knowledge of how to streamline the body so as to reduce water resistance will add to the over-all efficiency of a swimmer.

Fig. 2a.   Starting position

The push and glide while swimming on the back requires a high degree of conscious breath control to prevent water from entering the nose.

The feet are spread about hip width and on the same plane as the trunk. The balls of the feet are in contact with the wall. The head is held so that the ears are in contact with the insides of the upper arms. The arms are in a position of extreme flexion with the elbows extended fully.

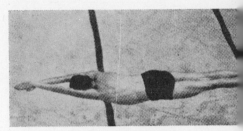

Fig. 2b.   Glide on front

This position results from the vigorous extension movements of the ankles, knees, and hips, and demonstrates a maximum effort to streamline the body.

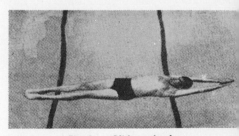

Fig. 2c.   Glide on back

This position, as in Fig. 2b, results from the vigorous extension movements of the ankles, knees, and hips. Considerable body control is required to maintain the streamlined position. Exclusion of water from the nose is achieved by controlled exhalation through the nostrils.

Underarm Side Stroke. This stroke is easily modified to become the basic life-saving stroke. It can be used for support as a resting stroke over a long period of time, or it can be used to cover considerable distance at a moderate, energy-conserving pace. The writer feels that by maintaining the positive action of the lower arm in a horizontal plane both the efficiency of the stroke and its adaptability to lifesaving are improved.

Fig. 3a. Glide

Data collected on 797 Springfield College freshmen disclosed the following concerning side-stroke preference:

366, or 45.92 per cent, preferred the right side and the top leg forward (regular) scissors

143, or 17.94 per cent, preferred the right side and the top leg backward (inverted) scissors

210, or 26.35 per cent, preferred the left side and the top leg forward (regular) scissors

78, or 9.79 per cent, preferred the left side and the top leg backward (inverted) scissors

There were a few students who preferred to use a vertical breast stroke kick while swimming on either side.

This position is maintained until the speed of the glide decreases noticeably. Exhalation through the nose is completed at this time.

Fig. 3b.   Positive action of right arm recovery of left arm and legs

Fig. 3c.   Positive action of legs, left arm, and recovery of right arm

Regular scissors (top leg forward) :

The right arm is pulled through a horizontal arc, about six inches under water, almost to the right hip. The left arm is recovered close to the chest to a point opposite the right shoulder, with the hand feathered, thumb side up. The hand is turned downward at the start. The legs are recovered by moving them into a stride position with knees flexed. Inhalation through the mouth occurs at this time.

The legs have started to move to-

gether, parallel to each other and to the surface of the water. The pressure surfaces of the bottom leg are the instep of the foot and the front of the leg. The pressure surfaces of the top leg are the sole of the foot and the back of the leg. The left arm is pulled through a vertical arc close to the chest. The right arm is recovered by flexing the elbow and pointing the fingers forward. Exhalation through the nose starts at this time.

Overarm Side Stroke. More efficient arm stroking is obtained with this stroke than is possible with the underarm side stroke. The overarm side stroke is excellent for approaching in rough water, or for making long approaches when speed without undue fatigue is essential. Two features of this stroke as it is shown in Fig. 4 are the completeness of the positive action of the lower arm, and the glide at the end of this positive action.

Fig. 4. Positive action of the right arm and recovery of left arm

Right Side:

The right arm is pulled through to the right hip in a horizontal arc about six inches underwater. The left arm is recovered above the surface during this action of the right arm, and the catch is made with the arm fully extended forward. The glide is executed after the completion of the positive action of the right arm, with the left arm in position for the catch, the legs held together in a streamlined position.

The right arm is recovered, after the completion of the positive action, by flexing the elbow, pointing the fingers forward, and then extending the elbow as the arm is moved forward to a position of extreme flexion. The left arm is pulled through a vertical arc to the left hip during the negative and positive actions of the legs. The initial phase of the recovery of the right arm coincides with the recovery of the legs. Inhalation through the mouth occurs during the positive action of the left arm and legs and exhalation through the nose during the glide.

Lifesaving Stroke. The transition to the lifesaving stroke from the underarm side stroke consists simply of holding the top arm in an extended position over the side of the upper thigh with the hand suspended just above the surface. The basic movements of the lower arm as employed in the underarm side stroke do not need to be changed. Long positive action of the stroking arm should be emphasized. Too often this action consists of alternate flexion and extension of the elbow joint instead of the efficient use of the powerful muscles which move the shoulder joint. The positive action of the lower arm should be based on the same principles as the positive action of the crawl arm stroke.

Regular scissors (top leg forward—right side): This positive phase of the arm action is similar to that used in the side stroke but the negative phase is modified to give greater support. The right arm is recovered by flexing the

Fig. 5a. Shallow arm pull

elbow, feathering the hand by turning the palm downward, and then extending the elbow fully to make the catch. The negative and positive actions of the right arm just precede those of the legs. The legs remain streamlined during the initial phase of the arm pull. Inhalation through the mouth occurs during the positive action of the right arm, and exhalation through the nose during the recovery of the arm.

most efficiently by the competent breast stroker, while the swimmer who has not mastered this kick will have more success with the inverted scissors kick.

Fig. 6.   Recovery of left arm and start of positive leg action

Fig. 5b.   Start of positive leg action

The leg action is identical to that used in the side stroke.

Inverted scissors (top leg back—left side) : The movements used in this stroke are identical to those used in Figs. 5a and 5b except that the body is turned over on the left side.

Legs Alone on Back. (See Fig. 7a) For using the legs alone while on the back, the two most efficient methods and the best adapted to lifesaving for most swimmers are the inverted breast-stroke kick and the inverted scissors kick. The inverted breast-stroke kick can be used

Fig. 7a.   Inverted scissors

The leg movements are identical with those used in Fig. 6 except that they are executed in a diagonal plane to permit the trunk to be turned on to the back.

Fig. 7b.   Inverted breast-stroke kick

These leg movements are identical with those used in Figs. 8c and 8d except that they are executed on the back.

Breast Stroke. The level of performance of this stroke is much below that of the side stroke, and yet no stroke is more important to the lifesaver than the breast stroke. Although many capable swimmers have not mastered the breast-stroke kick, in part at least because of inadequate instruction, every prospective lifesaver should be able at least to coordinate the component parts of the stroke correctly, even though one leg may revert to a scissors kick action. However, anyone who has progressed through the National YMCA Progressive Aquatic Tests may be expected to execute this stroke correctly. The face of the rescuer should be held out of water when this stroke is used for lifesaving purposes.

Fig. 8a. Glide

This position is maintained until the speed of the glide decreases noticeably. Exhalation through the nose takes place at this time.

Fig. 8b. Positive arm action

The straight arms, from a position about four inches underwater and with the palms of the hands turned outward at an angle of approximately forty-five degrees, are pulled diagonally lateralward, downward, and backward to a depth of about ten inches. This positive action stops when the hands reach a position about eight inches in front of the shoulders. Inhalation through the mouth occurs at this time.

Fig. 8c. Recovery of arms and start of positive leg action

The initial phase of the recovery of the arms is accomplished by flexing the elbows and pressing them against the ribs. The recovery of the legs, which is coincident with this phase of the arm action, consists of flexing the knees and spreading the legs until the feet are about a foot apart. The arms, with the thumbs in contact with each other, start forward to the glide position as the positive action of the legs begins. Exhalation through the nose starts at this time.

Fig. 8d. Positive leg action

From a position of complete recovery the legs are moved sideward, backward, and together in a continuous vigorous motion. The ankles are flexed and the feet are turned outward during the initial stage of the kick. As the kick nears completion the ankles are extended and the soles of the feet are turned inward. The propulsive surfaces are the insides of the legs and feet, and the soles of the feet. Exhalation through the nose is completed at this time.

Underwater Swimming. Although there are several methods of swimming underwater, the two methods most efficient for most swimmers are: (1) the modified breast-stroke method, Figs. 9a, 9b, 9c, and (2) the method employing the underwater breast-stroke arm action and the regular scissors kick. Coordination in both methods is identical. Two important features are the glide, Fig. 9b, and the complete arm pull, Figs. 9a and 9b. If there is danger of colliding with some underwater menace, the regular breast stroke is employed whenever lack of water clarity prevents adequate vision. Underwater depth may be decreased or increased by upward or downward action of the head, by extension or flexion of the trunk, by downward pressure during the initial phase of the positive action of the arms, and by upward pressure with the hands when the positive action of the arms is terminated. These movements may be combined or used singly, depending upon the degree of change desired.

Fig. 9a.   Positive arm action

The purpose of the initial phase of the arm pull which is shown in Fig. 8b is not only to produce propulsion but also to maintain the desired depth underwater. The initial phase is followed by some flexion of the elbows, which causes the hands to be directly under the shoulders

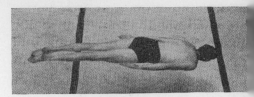

Fig. 9b.   Glide

during the most effective part of the arm pull. The pull is completed by the full extension of the elbows.

This position is maintained until the speed of the glide decreases noticeably. The upward position of the palms of the hands denotes effective application of the wrist action.

Fig. 9c.   Recovery of arms and start of positive leg action

The movements employed here are identical with those shown in Fig. 8c except for the lower head position. The arm pull follows immediately the positive action of the legs.

Elementary Back Stroke. As a resting stroke, the elementary back stroke can be used to ward off extreme fatigue while still providing slow but sustained progress. Breath control while swimming in smooth water is no problem, but if the water is rough and breaking over the swimmer's face conscious breath control is required. Although the type of leg action illustrated in Fig. 10b does not provide a strong propulsive reaction, it is easy to learn and will furnish support while the swimmer is relaxing. If a strong propulsive reaction is desired the inverted breast-stroke kick or inverted scissors kick should be used.

Fig. 10a. Glide

This position is maintained until the speed of the glide decreases noticeably. Exhalation through the nose occurs at this time. Maximum water displacement is accomplished by keeping the ears submerged.

Fig. 10b. Start of positive arm and leg action

The arms are recovered by drawing the fingers up the sides of the chest and extending the elbows sideward so that the hands are above shoulder level. Inhalation through the mouth occurs during the negative action of the arms. The straight arms are pulled through to the sides of the thighs at a depth of about four inches. The legs are recovered in a horizontal plane by partially flexing the knees and turning them outward, extending the ankles and spreading the legs fully. From the recovered position the knees are gradually extended as the legs are brought together sharply. The positive and negative actions of the arms and legs coincide. The pressure surfaces of the legs are the sides and back of the legs and soles of the feet.

Survival Position on Back. This skill will enable a swimmer with a minimum

of positive buoyancy to remain afloat for a long time while awaiting rescue. Support in this position is accomplished with a minimum expenditure of energy and may be resorted to following injury to one or both arms, injury to one leg, or incapacitating cramp in one leg. Such phase of disrobing as the removal of a heavy jacket, or shirt and trousers, may be carried out in this position. Breath control in smooth water poses no problem, but if the water is rough and breaking over the face conscious breath control is necessary.

Fig. 11. Supporting action of left leg, recovery of right leg

The body is supported in a horizontal stationary position by the alternate vertical action of the legs and a supporting action of the hands. More buoyant individuals may choose to hold the arms in the position demonstrated. The negative action of one leg coincides with the positive action of the other. The negative action consists of flexing the hip enough to cause the knee to just break the surface as the knee is gradually extended. The ankle is relaxed. The positive action consists of slight extension of the hip, complete flexion of the knee, and extension of the ankle. The pressure surfaces are the soles of the feet and the back of the legs, and the action is slow and moderate.

Survival Position on Front. Lanoue (83) has created and developed the best method of staying afloat easily for long periods of time. See Figs. 11a and 11b. His method employs such basic principles as: breath control, energy conservation, maximum displacement of water, and the law of interaction (to every action there is an equal and opposite reaction). The practicability of this method is attested by the results of carefully controlled experiments, of which one showed that sixty poor swimmers were able to remain afloat for an average of four hours and forty minutes and sixteen stayed afloat for eight hours. Even more remarkable is the fact that twenty of these poor swimmers had their wrists tied behind their backs, another twenty had their legs tied in a half bent position, and the remaining twenty were free. In the opinion of the writer this method should be taught to everyone, regardless of age, sex, or ability, and should serve as the core of all swimming programs.

Fig. 11b.   Breathing position

3. Exhale through the nose while (not before and not after) raising the head just high enough to get the chin out of the water. Keep shoulders underwater.

4. The instant the head is vertical, make the downward thrust which supports the body during the inhalation through the mouth.

5. As soon as the lungs are full, drop the face down to the horizontal, and immediately give another long, slow thrust backward and downward.

6. Relax with head, arms, and legs dangling, holding all air for four or five seconds while slowly floating forward and upward.

Fig. 11a.   Submerged position

In Lanoue's own words his method consists of:

1. With the lungs chock full, float face down, arms and legs dangling, with the back of the neck on the surface.

2. Get ready for a slow, easy, downward push, using arms, legs, or both.

Vertical Support. The ability to support oneself easily in a vertical position by the use of the legs alone (treading water), by the arms alone, or by the use of arms and legs together is basic to good watermanship. A close relationship has been observed between a two minute water-treading test and ability to complete the practical lifesaving test non-stop. Skill in treading water is highly important because of the numerous occasions in lifesaving when the arms are occupied in the performance of some necessary task.

For most swimmers the two most efficient kicks are the scissors kick and the breast-stroke kick. The speed and vigor of the kick depend upon body type (33, 116) and the degree of support required.

modified by keeping the elbows in the same horizontal plane as the hands and turning the thumb sides of the hands upward about thirty degrees to provide some downward pressure by the palms of the hands. The positive action of the legs is modified by not moving them together completely. This provides a more continuous supporting action. The speed and vigor of the leg and arm movements depend upon the degree of support needed.

Fig. 12. Whole stroke

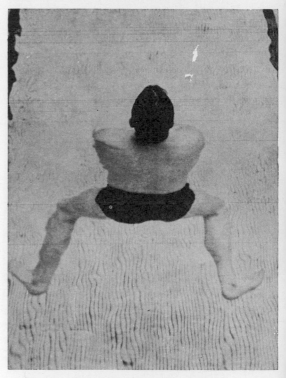

Fig. 13a. Legs alone, breast-stroke kick, start of positive leg action

The movements used in this stroke are identical to the basic movements used in the breast stroke except that support, rather than propulsion, is the objective. The recovery phase of the arm action is

The arms are folded on the chest and the legs execute the breast-stroke kick.

Fig. 13b. Completed leg action

The legs have completed the kick and have started to recover. To provide continuous support and to avoid a bobbing action, the legs are not moved together completely. The speed and vigor of the leg action depends upon the degree of support needed.

Fig. 14a. Legs alone, scissors kick, start of positive leg action

Fig. 14b. Completed leg action

The principles described for Fig. 13b apply here.

Floating. Ability to float motionless depends upon the following factors: conscious breath control, body type, regulation of the center of gravity, knowledge of the skill involved, and relaxation. Many capable swimmers never learn to float correctly because they fail to realize the importance of conscious breath control. Muscular and big-boned individuals experience considerable difficulty in learning to float, and some finally decide that it is a hopeless task. Persistent practice under proper guidance will, however, bring success in all but a very few of these cases if improvement in breath control is obtained, together with pos-

sible tissue changes and increased vital capacity.

The human body will float only when it has positive buoyancy, a specific gravity (S.G.) of less than one, which is the specific gravity of fresh water. Specific gravity is the ratio between the weight of the body and the weight of an equal volume of water. The S.G. of fresh water is 1.0, of sea water, 1.025, of lead, 11.3, and of iron, 7.86. When a submerged body displaces a weight of water greater than its own weight, that body will float. For example, a person who has a volume or bulk of 2.5 cu. ft. and weighs 154 pounds will displace 2.5 cu. ft. of fresh water weighing 156 pounds (2.5×62.4). His specific gravity, therefore, is $154 \div 156$ or .987, which is less than one, the specific gravity of fresh water. Position and ease in floating depend upon how much less than one specific gravity is. Cureton (32) states that the human body has an S.G. ranging from .970 to 1.20. He also states that muscle tissue has an S.G. of approximately 1.085, compact bone 1.90, and adipose tissue (fat) .700-.980, depending upon the ratio of fat cells to other types of connective tissue (50). Large and fat and slim individuals will therefore usually displace a weight of water greater than their own weight (S.G. less than 1.0), whereas muscular, big-boned individuals will displace a weight of water less than their own weight (S.G. more than 1.0).

An increase in volume without an appreciable increase in weight will lower the S.G. This happens when a life jacket is worn or when a swimmer takes a full inspiration of several seconds duration. It explains why most persons can float only when the lungs are full of air and also why controlled breathing is so important.

The swimmer with a large vital capacity can usually float horizontally (Fig. 15b) by lifting his hands partly out of the water. This action increases the weight moment at the head end and prevents the legs from sinking. The weight moment of the legs may be decreased by flexing the knees as shown in Fig. 15c. This is the action of a first class lever with the center of buoyancy acting as the fulcrum (32). Floating in sea water is easier than floating in fresh water because of the higher S.G. of sea water (1.025).

The swimmer familiar with the mechanics of floating makes a better emotional adjustment to the water and is able to conserve his energy through economy of motion. The laws of flotation may be summarized as follows (43):

1. A body sinks in water if the weight of the water it displaces is less than the weight of the body.

2. A submerged body remains in equilibrium, neither rising nor sinking, if the weight of the water it displaces exactly equals its own weight.

3. A body will float if it displaces a weight of water greater than its own weight.

Assume a diagonal support position, inhale fully, move the head back, arch the back, and slowly, under water, move the straight arms sideward with the palms turned upward. Controlled breathing consisting of quick but full exhalations and inhalations, followed by a brief period of breath holding, is essential for those individuals who possess slight positive buoyancy.

Fig. 15b.   Horizontal floating

Assume a horizontal support position, inhale fully; slowly, under water, move the straight arms close to the head and flex the wrists slightly to bring the hands out of water. Hold the breath until equilibrium is reached, and then continue with controlled breathing. This

Fig. 15c.   Horizontal floating

type of floating is only possible for those individuals who possess sufficient positive buoyancy, breath control, and body control.

Surface Dives. The two types of surface dives are: head foremost and feet foremost. The head foremost surface dive may be executed either from a pike (jackknife) position, or from a tuck position, depending upon preference. If the lifesaver is forced to dive repeatedly, the tuck surface dive usually requires

Fig. 15a.   Angle floating

less expenditure of energy than the pike surface dive. The tuck dive differs from the pike dive only in the tucking action of the legs following the bending of the trunk. The head foremost surface dive should be employed only in known waters, and even then a short arm stroke should be used to avoid possible injury to the face and head if the water depth should be misjudged, or a rock or stump should be encountered.

The feet foremost surface dive should be used whenever the lifesaver has any doubt about the water depth or conditions at the bottom. The technique illustrated in Figs. 17a and 17b is also used for the breath control drill called bobbing.

When the approach swim is short, and haste is imperative, the lifesaver may proceed directly into a surface dive from the crawl stroke.

trunk is flexed to the vertical. The head is held well back with the eyes fixed on the bottom.

Fig. 16b. Going down

Fig. 16a. Pike position

Head first:

From the start of the breast-stroke glide, the straight arms are pulled backward horizontally to the hips as the

Support for the lifting movement of the straight legs to the vertical is provided by turning the palms of the hands downward, and maintaining downward pressure as the arms are moved to a streamlined position beyond the head. The descent is in the vertical plane and is caused by the weight of the legs above the surface. A depth of about ten feet can be reached by most individuals without resorting to swimming movements.

Fig. 17a. Lift

Feet first:

From the vertical support position the straight arms are pulled downward in the frontal plane to the sides of the thighs simultaneously with the positive action of the legs. This combined positive action of the arms and legs will cause the head, shoulders, and upper portion of the trunk to be lifted above the surface. The speed and depth of the descent depends in large measure upon the extent of the lift and the streamlined position of the body.

Fig. 17b. Going down

To achieve maximum depth with one side-upward, overhead sweep of the arms, the arm action is delayed until a depth of about two feet has been reached with the arms still pressed tightly against the sides of the body. The legs are straight and together, the ankles are fully extended, and the toes pointed, to assure a maximum depth. If a greater depth is desired than one positive arm action permits, the arms are recovered by flexing the elbows fully as they are moved downward against the sides of the chest. The hands are then moved downward to the starting position against the sides of the thighs in preparation for another positive arm action.

4.

Recovery of a Submerged Victim

INTRODUCTION

If the recovery of a submerged victim is to be successful, intelligent, well-directed haste on the part of the rescuer is imperative. Just how long a victim can remain under water and still survive is undeterminable. Where one person may fail to survive a submersion of two minutes or less another person may be revived after being under water thirty minutes (9). Keith (80) compiled the following data concerning 401 cases of drowning:

PERIOD OF IMMERSION

	1 to 5 min.	*6 to 10 min.*	*11 to 15 min.*	*Over 15 min.*
Successful cases of restoration	234	89	12	4
Unsuccessful cases	13	21	12	16

Gonzales (54) states: "the process of drowning usually takes about three to five minutes, but may be prolonged to ten minutes or more." The American Red Cross (2) states that "more than ninety per cent of all submerged victims must be brought to the surface within ten minutes of their submersion if they are to have a reasonable chance to survive." Karpovich (71) concluded that "the average length of submersion after which resuscitation is doubtful, if not impossible, is probably about five minutes. This however does not mean that

we should not attempt a resuscitation if the victim has remained under water more than half an hour." He (71) also states: "Whenever a question arises as to how long a drowned person remained under water we usually deal with guesses. How often has an actual drown-been clocked, even accidentally? And it is a fact of common experience that when the emotions are aroused in an emergency, the estimation of time becomes grossly distorted and a minute may seem much longer than a mere sixty seconds. We should constantly bear this in mind in order to appraise critically the reports coming even from those people whose reliability is beyond any doubt."

Although authorities may differ as to what constitutes the exact duration of a fatal submersion the rescuer must act quickly unless it is clearly evident that the victim has been under water for an hour or more (2).

DIVING RECOVERY

Consideration by the rescuer of such factors as: distance to be swum, water clarity, water temperature, presence of currents, and his own physical fitness and skill should result in a sensible course of action. Common sense dictates that the rescuer should arrive at the place where the victim was last seen, ready to surface dive and remain under water long enough, at least, to make a brief search. A hurried approach swim that leaves the rescuer so fatigued that he must recuperate will result in the loss of precious time.

During the approach swim the rescuer should fix his eyes on the spot where the victim was last seen. Air bubbles may rise to the surface from the lungs or clothing of the victim or from the bottom, if it is disturbed, to serve as a guide to the rescuer. Of course, time should not be lost seeking a face mask but one should be used if immediately available. The face mask should become a standard piece of lifesaving equipment and every lifesaver should be trained in its use.

As soon as the rescuer arrives at the place where the victim was last seen he may overbreathe several times before surface diving and searching the bottom. At times, of course, the victim may be several feet under the surface and, if this is the case, the rescuer should surface dive immediately. In strange waters where the bottom cannot be seen, the rescuer should use the feet foremost surface dive to avoid possible injury to the face or head. If the water is clear the rescuer may dive feet foremost or head foremost depending upon his preference. If the victim is not located on the first dive, the rescuer may be mistaken in the place where he thought the victim disappeared. When this is the case the rescuer should scan the bottom by swimming slowly along the surface with his face in the water, covering the area in a series of back and forth, parallel, overlapping lanes until the victim is located or the rescuer is satisfied that the victim is not in that area. This procedure is possible, of course, only when the water is clear. When lack of water clarity does not permit scanning the bottom from the surface, the rescuer will be forced to cover the area by surface diving repeatedly and swimming near the bottom, depending entirely upon feeling his way along. To conserve his energy the rescuer should not stay under water for an extended period at any one time, but should plan to cover a distance of about twenty feet before returning to the surface to prepare for another surface dive. Again, the rescuer should cover the area in a series of back-and-forth, parallel, overlapping lanes until the victim is located or the recuer is satisfied that the victim is not in that area.

The rescuer should enlist the aid of several competent observers whenever possible, in order to speed up the rescue procedure. It is evident that the efforts of several capable rescuers working in close co-operation side by side will be a definite improvement over the efforts of just one rescuer. A shallow water area can be quickly covered by a group of swimmers who line up abreast and walk straight ahead, searching the bottom with their feet. They may even progress into deeper water where group co-ordinated surface diving is necessary.

Considerable misunderstanding exists concerning the length of time the breath can be held under water and the depth to which one can dive without the benefit of diving dress. The rescuer who is accurately informed on these points is less likely to act in a foolhardy manner and more likely to complete a difficult recovery. Every rescuer should know his limitations and never take any unnecessary chances.

Berge and Lanier (11) observe with regard to deep diving that "the ability to dive deeply is not very common, and takes long training to develop. In the Bandas the natives rarely go down more than twenty to thirty feet. Years later, at another island, I did see an expert skin diver swim down to 120 feet, and I timed him for three minutes in all. But that was a stunt." Hall (63) gives an account of two pearl divers who demonstrated their skill to him. "The two men, holding to the side of the canoe, breathed deeply for a half minute or so, filling their lungs again and again, then they went down. Viggo had let out 100 feet of line. . . . I timed the dive. One man was under water one minute thirty-five seconds and the other one minute forty-eight seconds. Viggo told me that dives from two minutes to two minutes and twenty seconds were common, and that three minutes was the longest one he had ever timed. He also told me that he had known divers to go as deep as thirty fathoms (180 feet) but that they could not work at such a depth." Dawson (38) points out that "in relation to diving, the studies of the 'Ama,' or professional Japanese women diver, are full of interest. With no protection but a glass apparatus for the eyes and nose, she can remain under water at a pressure of 3.5 atmospheres (equal to 51.45 pounds per square inch, which is equivalent to a water depth of 115.5 feet of sea water or 118.9 feet of fresh water) for 2.5 minutes and can do severe physical work in a condition of asphyxia. Her expired air on returning to the surface contains three per cent oxygen (under normal conditions expired air contains approximately 16.2 per cent oxygen). The duration of her descent is 17-20 seconds and of ascent 13-18 seconds, but these rapid changes seem to cause no damage."

The writer was granted permission by the Navy Department in the summer of 1946 to take part in the escape training at the U. S. Navy Submarine School at New London, Connecticut. The escape tank is a cylindrical steel tower, approximately eighteen feet in diameter, 138 feet high, containing 100 feet of filtered, chlorinated fresh water heated to a temperature of approximately ninety degrees F. We were taught how to use the Momsen Lung, a device that supplies oxygen through a two-way valve and rubber mouthpiece to the trainee. Before an escape is made the mouthpiece

is carefully fitted, the oxygen container is charged, and the nostrils are pinched shut by a sturdy nose clip. The trainee then ducks out through the escape hatch, grasps the line, and slowly floats to the surface at the rate of fifty feet per minute. During this time he is under the close scrutiny of instructors to see that he is following the escape procedure correctly. To avoid injury to the lungs, and air embolism, the trainee must breathe in and out of "the lung" to equalize the air pressure within his lungs with their gradually decreasing water pressure. Before taking part in the escape training the trainee must show that he can withstand a pressure of fifty pounds per square inch (equivalent to water depth of 115.6 feet) in the compression chamber. In conjunction with this training the writer had an excellent opportunity to observe the Navy instructors descend to the bottom of the tank (one hundred feet) wearing only goggles and a nose clip. There is much to be learned from these men concerning methods of descent and ascent and breath-holding. Lieutenant Robertson, U.S.N., who is an authority on these matters, is able to descend to the bottom of the tank in approximately seventeen seconds. He uses a feet foremost surface dive, the initial action of which carries him well below the surface. He may repeat the arm action several times, but when he reaches a depth of thirty feet he holds his arms overhead for balance as he continues to descend. According to Lieutenant Robertson, he loses his positive buoyancy at about eighteen feet and sinks to the bottom from that depth. Positive buoyancy is lost because water pressure compresses the air in the body, which causes the specific gravity of the body to increase until it exceeds that of fresh water or sea water. Although the depth at which positive buoyancy is lost varies with individuals, positive buoyancy will be lost, at a depth of thirty-three feet in sea water or thirty-four feet in fresh water.

The ascent at the escape tower is made either by swimming to the surface, which is quite fatiguing, or by coming up a line hand over hand. The latter method is speedy, some instructors having come to the surface from the bottom (one hundred feet) in ten seconds.

Concerning breath-holding, Berge and Lanier (11) say: "Three minutes seems to be the limit of the best skin divers, if they're doing any work, whether it's at forty feet or a hundred. I've always had a belief that an occasional expert might be able as a stunt to stay down five minutes, keeping perfectly quiet; but I've never seen it done."

To prolong his stay under water the rescuer should resort to hyperventilation (overbreathing) for a short period before surface diving. Hyperventilation consists of 10-15 deep and rapid respirations with emphasis on the expiratory phase. Dawson (38) says: "It may be stated that if one breathes violently for some time and then holds the breath, it is found that the irresistible impulse to begin breathing is considerably postponed." [A person who normally has no difficulty in holding his breath for one minute finds that after a dozen or so deep and rapid respirations he has no difficulty in extending his breath-holding 50 per cent or more.] Forced ventilation of the lungs causes a reduction of the carbon dioxide in the blood which in turn causes a decrease in the respiratory movements. Karpovich (78) points out: "The question arises whether carbon dioxide has any specific action on the respiratory center or whether it acts solely by virtue of its effect on the hydrogen-ion concentration of the blood. An addition of carbon dioxide to the blood causes an apparent greater effect upon the respiration than do acids. This has been interpreted as meaning that carbon dioxide acts as a respiratory

stimulus, not solely because it dissolves in the blood to form carbonic acid and thus give rise to hydrogen-ions, but because it has some specification apart from this property."

There is some danger in prolonged hyperventilation at any one time and consequently the rescuer should avoid any excess in this direction (27, 37, 50, 98). Dawson (38) points out that, "overbreathing in respect to O_2 produces no untoward effects, but the blowing off of an unusual amount of CO_2 may, if sufficiently excessive, even cause convulsions."

Berge and Lanier (11) relate an interesting account of hyperventilation: "When you see a lot of skin divers working from their canoes you can hear them 'taking the wind' in preparation. A man gathers himself together, his face works, he gulps and groans and strains as he forces his diaphragm downward and pumps air into his lungs, like a compressor, and holds it there. I never knew a white man who had reached a real mastery of that trick." Hall (63) gives the following account of hyperventilation: "The two men, holding to the side of the canoe, breathed deeply for half a minute or so, filling their lungs again and again; they they went down."

Even though a rescuer has sufficient breath-holding capacity and courage to conduct a bottom search in twenty-five feet of water he is only partially prepared to dive to that depth. He must know the technique of increasing the pressure on the internal surfaces of the ear drums to equal that of the increasing water pressure on the external surfaces. The technique of equalizing the pressure is known variously as "popping the ears," "blowing the ears," or "cracking the ears." The following explanation of the anatomy of the ear will help the rescuer to understand better what happens when he "pops his ears": "The (44) middle ear or tympanic cavity is an air-filled cavity in the petrous portion of the temporal bone. It is separated from the outside air by the tympanic membrane or ear drum and communicates with the nasal part of the pharynx (common passageway for air and food) by means of the auditory or Eustachian tube (length about 36mm.) which serves to equalize the pressure on the tympanic membrane. The external ear consists of a cartilaginous framework, the auricle and a canal, the external auditory meatus, which leads inward to the ear drum."

To "pop the ears" the rescuer closes his mouth, pinches his nostrils shut with his fingers or, better when surface divings, with a sturdy nose clip, and attempts to exhale. This effort to exhale forces air into the Eustachian tubes, if no congestion is present, and on into the tympanic cavity, which results in equalizing the pressure on the ear drums. If a tightly fitting nose clip is worn with goggles or a face mask, the hands will be free to execute whatever movements are necessary without interference. "Popping the ears" can be accomplished when wearing just a face mask by closing the mouth, holding the mask firmly against the nose and face, and attempting to exhale.

"Popping the ears" should start at about five feet under water and should continue regularly every four or five feet during the descent. A slight hissing sound indicates that air has entered the middle ears. A rescuer should not attempt to dive deeply or to equalize pressure on his ears when troubled with a nose or throat infection. If he does, he may spread the infection to the middle ears by forcing infected matter into the Eustachian tubes, or he may rupture his ear drums because the Eustachian tubes are blocked and no air can be forced through them to equalize the water pressure. Of course he may find that he cannot dive more than a few

feet because of excruciating ear pains. An extreme hazard is a ruptured ear drum, which may allow contaminated water to pass into the middle ear. In addition there is some evidence to show that cold water entering the middle ear through a ruptured ear drum can cause dizziness (51, 146) and possible death.

A natural question to raise is to what depth the rescuer can descend safely. The answer depends on such factors as physical fitness, skill, water clarity, water temperature, and safety precautions. Generally speaking, a senior lifesaver who is physically fit and who is thoroughly familiar with the necessary techniques should be able to descend to a depth of approximately twenty-five feet when the water is warm and reasonably clear. A junior lifesaver who has met the same standards should be able to descend to a depth of approximately fifteen feet when the water is warm and reasonably clear. Whenever possible, however, the rescuer should work with a life line, tied with a bowline knot, so that he can be pulled to safety by an assistant in a boat or on a float, if an unusual situation should occur. Berge and Lanier (11) vividly describe what happens when a diver exceeds his breath-holding limit: "The young skin diver's greatest danger is over-staying under water. Frequently, as a result, he collapses as he nears the surface. More than once I have seen a man come up right beside the canoe and suddenly, just before he broke water, his limbs relaxed, and his body looked as if it had a paralytic stroke, all the remaining air rushed out of his lungs; and he began to sink slowly. If there's nobody at hand to jump in and rescue him, he sinks to the bottom and drowns."

One instructor the writer talked to at the escape tower remained under water at the bottom of the tank (one hundred feet) for nearly three minutes during a demonstration, but lost consciousness about twenty-five feet from the surface on the way up. Of course he was under the constant observation of the other instructors and was quickly picked up and taken into a diving bell where he was soon revived. He had been under water about three minutes and ten seconds, and had exceeded his customary limit. He remarked that he felt himself growing weaker and was unable to pull himself up the line no matter how hard he tried. He would have drowned if he had been alone, or if he had been observed by the usual untrained bystander.

Similar observations have been made at Springfield College following a fifty-yard swim under water after hyperventilation. In several cases where progress was slow and the breath-holding capacity while swimming was about one minute, the swimmer would come to the surface, move jerkily, and then lose consciousness. Drowning would have resulted if immediate aid had not been at hand.

Although there are numerous accounts of prolonged breath-holding under water, the rescuer should not attempt to exceed a stay of one minute. In fact he will work more efficiently if he does not attempt to remain under water for prolonged periods. Prolonged breath-holding while exercising may cause such an oxygen deficit that the rescuer wastes time recuperating. The question of possible heart strain during vigorous physical activity also arises. Regarding this possibility Karpovich (78) states: Parsonnet and Bernstein reviewed the question of heart strain during physical activity. Their conclusion was that there is no scientific proof of pathological chronic heart strain resulting from the cumulative effects of hard muscular work. Hypertrophy (enlargement) merely indicates a better development of the heart muscle—work hypertrophy."

Two potent psychological factors which play an important part in under-water recovery are water clarity and water temperature. When the water is clear so that the bottom can be seen and warm enough to be comfortable, the rescuer can carry out the recovery procedures without much difficulty. However, if the water is murky and the rescuer must feel his way along the bottom he will be handicapped psychologically and his underwater efficiency is likely to be reduced considerably.

One method of picking up a victim from a prone position on the bottom is to grasp him by the upper arm, close to the armpit. In essence the rescuer will use a type of rear approach. Other methods are the chin grasp, hair grasp, and clothing grasp, depending upon the preference of the rescuer and the position of the victim. If the victim is on his back the rescuer may use the wrist grasp or upper-arm grasp type of front approach, depending upon the position of the victim's arms. The rescuer, therefore, must be alert for any attempt on the part

Fig. 18.   Upper arm grasp

of the victim to grab him. It is possible, of course, for the rescuer to approach a victim who is on his back from the head end; this will permit a type of rear approach, rather than an approach from above. The rescuer should be well trained in several methods so as to be able to adapt himself quickly to any situation.

Because every second is precious, a speedy return to the surface after picking up the victim is of paramount importance. If the bottom is firm the rescuer should place his feet against it and execute a vigorous push-off toward the surface. If the bottom is muddy or weedy the rescuer will have to rely entirely upon a swimming ascent.

Recovery Equipment

Grappling Irons. Scully (17) makes the following observation: "The use of grappling irons in body recovery is a very important part of the lifesaver's training, for the grappling iron has been a much misunderstood device. It has been too often associated with death rather than with the fact that it may be used to recover the body of the apparently drowned person in time to resuscitate him. This is especially true where the water is too deep for surface diving. There are a number of cases on record of an apparently drowned person who has been recovered by this apparatus, and has been successfully revived. The grappling iron, contrary to general belief, rarely hooks anyone in a vital place. It usually catches the person in the muscles or in the bathing suit or clothing, and as the body under the water is quite light, it does not injure it to any extent in bringing it up. It is a real lifesaving device."

Dragging operations should start a short distance from the spot where the victim was last seen, and several careful but quick tries should be made. If the recovery is successful no time should be lost in lifting the victim into the boat and starting resuscitation immediately.

In case the initial efforts are unsuccessful, and there is some question just where the victim went down, a systematic coverage of the area should be started. Effective dragging requires the close co-operation of the oarsman and the rescuer. The rescuer sits in the stern of the rowboat (a square stern is most suitable), and plays out the line until the irons are on the bottom. The oarsman gets under way slowly, maintaining a straight course, and constantly on the alert for commands from the rescuer. When the outer boundary of the area is reached the oarsman turns and rows a parallel, overlapping course back to the starting point. This procedure is repeated until the area is thoroughly covered. If the victim is not located, the same area may be searched again or a new area selected, depending upon the evidence at hand.

When the rescuer feels the line tighten in his hand he immediately commands the oarsman to stop and backwater as he hauls in on the line until it is perpendicular. If the irons do not lift readily, the rescuer may assume that some heavy or immovable object has been hooked. Careful maneuvering may enable the rescuer to unhook the irons, or it may be necessary to bend or break off a hook by yanking vigorously on the line.

Occasionally the irons should be hauled to the surface and inspected to prevent weeds or other debris from fouling the hooks.

Fig. 19. Grappling irons
(Courtesy of George C. Adams)

Two sets of grappling irons are shown here, one assembled ready to use, and the other disassembled in the canvas bag. These irons are easily carried and can be quickly assembled. If a hook should penetrate the victim's skin, that cluster of hooks can be quickly unhooked from the cross bar and the chain tied or taped in position. This feature will save precious seconds because no time will be lost attempting to remove the hook, and an ugly wound may be avoided by removing the hooks carefully at a later time.

The Aqua-Lung. During the past three years the Aqua-Lung has become widely used by amateur spear fishermen and minor salvage operators. Although the Aqua-Lung is expertly designed and has been thoroughly tested, nevertheless human error is still such an important factor that every aquatic instructor should know the correct operating procedures

as well as the effects of underwater pressure in order that he may provide proper instruction for the novice.

In addition to the recreational and utilitarian uses of the Aqua-Lung there is the humanitarian or lifesaving function which should be recognized by specially trained individuals and rescue groups. There are many accident situations that terminate fatally for want of a lifesaver trained in winter and summer underwater rescue and recovery procedures.

The Aqua-Lung (26, 45) is a self-contained diving unit consisting of one or two compressed air cylinders (never use oxygen for diving) each of which contains 70 cubic feet of air at maximum pressure. The standard one-tank model will permit a diver to stay at a depth of 33 feet under ordinary circumstances for approximately fifty minutes. The automatic demand regulator, which is the heart of the Aqua-Lung, permits inhalation through a flexible, non-kinking hose, only as needed at a pressure identical to the depth pressure. This flexible hose connects to the mouthpiece which is held firmly by the teeth and lips. A second flexible hose may be used to carry off the exhaled air and eliminates the possibility of carbon dioxide accumulation which can cause discomfort and danger to the diver.

Strict observation of the following rules will reduce human error and permit the diver to dive safely:

1. The diver must be a competent swimmer (minimum standard—shark test) in good condition.

2. The diver should check all his equipment carefully for proper function and quick release, particularly the weight belt, before entering the water.

3. The diver should never dive alone and before entering the water should always check the air pressure to be certain there is an adequate supply. Use only compressed air, never oxygen.

4. The diver after entering the water should not descend until another check is made of all equipment and the regulator is functioning properly when fully submerged.

5. The diver should not descend more rapidly than the water pressure on the eardrums can be equalized by "popping the ear," which can be accomplished by swallowing or blowing through the nose while holding the face mask tightly against the face. Stop the descent at the first signs of discomfort and "pop the ears"; if not successful, ascend five feet and try again. If not successful after three or four attempts at shallower levels, do not dive at all. Even a slight cold will prevent air from entering the Eustachian tubes.

6. Divers should use the buddy system and stay within sight of each other. If the water is so murky that visual contact is impractical, use connecting safety lines.

Fig. 20. The SCUBA Diver

7. The beginning diver should be conservative at all times and should not attempt to dive below 50 feet. All divers should be familiar with the Safety Curve and Decompression Tables (138).

8. The diver should learn how to blow out, through the exhaling valve, water, which may seep into his mouth, by rolling onto his left side. Smaller quantities may be swallowed.

9. The diver should avoid undue exertion under water which causes fatigue and excessive air consumption.

10. The diver can avoid dangerous air pressure in the lungs by breathing regularly during the ascent. Never hold the breath. Also, slow up the ascent when near the surface and take at least 90 seconds to ascend the last 35 feet. Exhale continuously during an emergency free ascent.

11. The diver who is out of air after the ascent to the surface should swim on his back to prevent the weight of the tank from tiring him.

Face Mask, Snorkle, and Flippers. The face mask is an invaluable aid to the rescuer performing an underwater recovery. Several safety types are on the market, and it is a simple matter to learn how to use one properly. The head strap should be adjusted to assure a sufficiently snug fit to prevent water from seeping inside the mask. Fogging on the inside of the mask can be prevented by rubbing saliva on the inside and rinsing lightly or by using a special non-fogging preparation that is rubbed or sprayed on and wiped with a dry cloth or towel.

As an aid to "popping the ears," face masks are available with finger and thumb indentations that permit the rescuer to pinch his nostrils shut while the face mask is in position, eliminating the necessity of wearing a nose clip.

The snorkle is a surface breathing tube usually made of plastic with a rubber mouthpiece and ball attachment which seals the tube and prevents water from entering when the swimmer is submerged. The snorkle is used with the face mask and permits the swimmer to breathe on the surface while keeping his face under water, thus avoiding the glare of sunlight and enabling him to dive immediately when the object is sighted.

There are several types of flippers on the market. Whether to use them or not

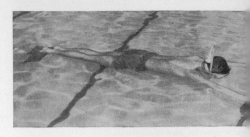

Fig. 21. Face mask, snorkle, and flippers

depends upon the preference of the rescuer. If used, it is necessary, to enjoy maximum efficiency, that the rescuer have flippers which fit properly. A desirable feature of some flippers is the adjustable and replaceable heel straps. Several long swims while wearing flippers are usually necessary before a correct fit can be made. Flippers which fit properly do not cause chafing or cramps, and do not interfere with the circulation of the feet. If chafing persists, even when the flippers fit well, wearing a pair of light socks or using adhesive tape to protect the affected parts will usually suffice. The flutter kick is the most efficient with flippers, although they can also be used effectively with the scissors kicks. For underwater swimming it is seldom necessary for the rescuer to use his arms, although he may use the flutter kick and the complete double arm pull correctly co-ordinated with a glide. But for most rescuers a continuous flutter kick action is too fatiguing to be practicable. Another style is to combine the complete double arm pull with a combination scissors kick and flutter kick co-ordinated correctly with a glide.

Flippers can be used to great advantage for treading water, surface diving, towing, underwater searching, and supporting a tired swimmer.

Search Board. The search board, when available, provides quicker coverage than the water glass, although the latter is a useful device to have on the water front. To increase the search board's effectiveness, a light but sturdy line twenty-five feet long should be attached to the board and held by the rescuer, to prevent the board from drifting away after he leaves it to recover the victim from the bottom.

Fig. 22. Search board (Courtesy of Desco)

This equipment is very helpful in locating the victim quickly in clear water. The rescuer scans the bottom through the face piece as he paddles the board over the area where the victim was last seen. A circular piece of glass about twenty inches in diameter is fitted into the bottom of the board and as the bottom of the board is beneath the surface, the water surface under the board is smooth and the bottom shows up clearly.

Marking Buoy. Prompt and accurate marking of the spot where the victim was last seen is absolutely necessary if a successful recovery is to be made. Frequently this is not done because no simple but practical device is immediately available for this purpose. A marking buoy should be part of the essential equipment of every water front.

This device shown consists of a weighted number ten can, a wooden cross piece to which the line is attached, fifty feet of light but strong line, and the float around which the line is wound. The spot where the victim was last seen is marked by dropping the marking buoy overboard. The weighted can sinks to the bottom as the line unwinds on the

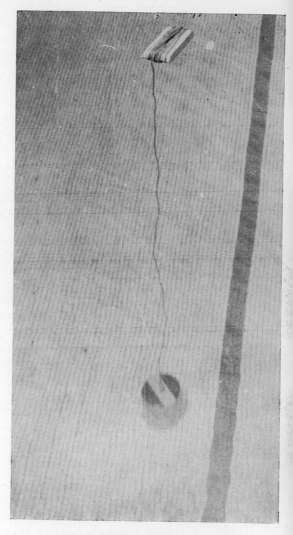

Fig. 23. Marking buoy
(Courtesy of George C. Adams)

float. If every five feet of the line is marked, the water depth can be quickly determined.

Underwater Flashlight. The immediate availability of an underwater light to be used for conducting an underwater search after nightfall can mean the difference between life and death. Such an underwater light can be easily made and when used in conjunction with the face

Fig. 24. Underwater flashlight
(Courtesy of George C. Adams)

mask will permit the rescuer to carry out an effective underwater search which would otherwise be quite impossible.

The device shown is a glass jar covered with electrician's tape to make the sides lightproof, a handle on the side near the top held on by the tape, a flashlight, a fitting to make the flashlight fit snugly into the jar, and the top of the glass jar. To use this device the flashlight is turned on and placed in the glass jar so that the light will shine through the bottom. The fitting is then inserted, and the top to the jar screwed on securely to make it watertight. A light line is secured to the handle so that the flashlight can be lowered to the bottom.

BODY RECOVERY

There are times when the procedures previously explained prove inadequate or are impossible to carry out. If the accident has occurred in a deep water lake where the water depth and tempera-

ture exceed the limits of surface diving recovery and grapplings has proved to be ineffective, the services of a professional diver will be necessary to recover the body. In excessively deep water no immediate recovery is possible because a body will sink to the bottom, regardless of the depth of the water, when its specific gravity exceeds that of water. "Water (43) is so nearly incompressible that it takes the stupendous pressure of twenty tons to reduce the volume of one cubic inch by only 0.1. This means that the water at the bottom of the ocean is only slightly more dense than it is near the surface."

Some bodies are never recovered, because deep water lakes and the ocean act as giant refrigerators, and apparently the disintegration of the body takes place without affecting its specific gravity sufficiently to cause it to float. For example, "the (133) settling of cold water in winter gives to the bottom of deep lakes a temperature around thirty-nine degrees throughout the year. While fresh water ceases sinking at thirty-nine degrees, salt water continues to increase in density, and therefore to sink almost until its freezing point is reached. For this reason ocean bottom water is much colder than that on the bottom of lakes; it may, in fact, be as low as twenty-nine degrees. The temperature in the Atlantic at a depth of 2000 fathoms (12,000 feet) is thirty-five degrees; but in the Gulf of Mexico, at that depth, only 39.5°, which is the temperature at the depth of the barrier (1000 fathoms) over which the water enters the Gulf from the Atlantic. The same relations prevail in the Mediterranean."

In warm water putrefaction of the body forms gases (carbon dioxide, methane, hydrogen-sulphide) (49) within the tissues, causing the specific gravity of the body to become lower than that of water (fresh water 1.0, sea water 1.025). When these changes occur, the body will rise to the surface and float. However, if a body is partially buried in mud or sand, or is held by some underwater obstruction, it may be prevented from coming to the surface. In such cases dynamite (2) has been used successfully by experts to dislodge the body when putrefaction had progressed far enough so that the body would rise to the surface.

Superstition formed the basis of many curious methods of body recovery used in years past. An article (41) written over fifty years ago reveals several interesting superstitions. "In Brittany when the body of a drowned man cannot be found, a lighted taper is fixed to a loaf of bread, which is then abandoned to the retreating current. When the loaf stops, there it is supposed the body will be recovered. The Indians imagine that in the case of a drowned body, its place may be discovered by floating a chip of cedar wood, which will stop and turn round over the exact spot. In Java, a live sheep is thrown into the water, and is supposed to indicate the position of the body by sinking near it. A curious custom is practised in Norway, where those in search of a drowned body row to and fro with a cock in the boat, fully expecting that the bird will crow when the boat reaches the spot where the corpse lies. The dead body of a drowned person may be ascertained by floating a loaf weighted with quicksilver, which is said at once to swim towards and stand over, the spot where the body lies." Today, these methods seem ludicrous and no one who has received lifesaving training would resort to them.

5.

Personal Safety

Introduction

The organic, neuro-muscular, and emotional benefits that are derived from swimming and diving are made possible only by accurate knowledge of the safety factors that govern where to swim, how much to swim, and when to swim.

Unintelligent participation in swimming and diving is extremely hazardous and can result in death. Because death is a possibility, fear becomes a very potent factor in the behavior of the individual when an emergency arises, and it is a factor which cannot be discounted. Fear, however, should not be the basis of learning personal safety factors because such a basis places restrictions on the clear thinking that is essential to the solution of an emergency situation. When reason is the basis of learning personal safety factors, the cause-result relationships provide the learner with a foundation on which to build the structure of clear thinking in an emergency. The initial impact of panic, powerful as it may be, will then be dissipated against the barrier of reason.

The achievement of personal safety in swimming is based upon the accumulation of sufficient correct knowledge concerning water conditions, plus sound judgment, and the development of adequate skill so that adaptability to a wide variety of circumstances is possible.

Where to Swim

Choosing a safe place to swim may be simply a matter of deciding which one of several adequately posted and skillfully supervised places will be patronized. This decision will place the swimmer, novice, and non-swimmer under the watchful eyes of trained personnel whose constant vigilance compensates in a large measure for the lack of good judgment on the part of many people. Here under supervision it is possible to deviate from the rule of "don't swim alone," but strict adherence to this rule is of paramount importance when swimming in an unsupervised area.

The decision to swim or bathe in an unsupervised area is unwise unless some member of the group is a qualified life saver. A preliminary survey of water and bottom conditions in any case should be made if the area is new to the group, in order to check on possible hazardous conditions.

Regardless of whether the swimmer chooses a supervised or unsupervised area for a swim, he should use sound judgment as a basis for his activity and not engage in any foolhardy exploits. The non-swimmer should be governed by an ultra-conservative attitude that confines his activity to shallow water. He should refrain from venturing into deep water with any artificial supports because to do so is to invite disaster. The non-swimmer who slips out of an inner tube into deep water will drown unless aid is immediately available.

All unknown waters should be entered cautiously; wade rather than dive, and always avoid the spectacular running plunge.

Rip Currents. To swim safely from an ocean beach, everyone, expert as well as the non-swimmer, must familiarize himself with the existing hazards.

The hazard that causes the greatest number of rescues (90, 118) is the "rip current." Nicholls (90) studied the causes of rescues over a ten-year period (1929-1938) for the Los Angeles City Beaches; out of a total of 2,830 rescues, 704, or 24.87 per cent, were necessitated by rip tides (rip currents). As a further indication of the hazardous nature of currents, 507, or 17.91 per cent, of the rescues were caused by lagoon and under pier currents. The next hazard while swimming is exhaustion in surf, which accounted for 226, or 7.98 per cent, of the rescues.

Shepard et al. (118) define and explain rip currents as . . .

seaward moving streaks of water which return the water carried landward by waves. These currents are believed to be an almost universal accompaniment of large waves breaking on an exposed coast. They are known as "rip tides" or "sea pusses," but the name "rip current" was proposed as being more appropriate. The term "rip" might also be used as an abbreviation, which removes the unfortunate tidal connotation of the popular term "rip tide." According to available evidence they appear to take the place erroneously assigned to undertow, in that they return the water which tends to be piled onto the beach by the waves and in doing this carry seaward fine sediment derived from the land. Rip currents are ordinarily fed by water moving along the shore from either side. The two currents join and extend out

in what is known as the "neck," where water rushes through the breakers in a narrow lane. Beyond the breakers the current spreads out in what is called the "head" and dissipates. The outward moving columns can be recognized by their brownish color if they contain abundant sediment, by their agitated water, or by an extension of foam belts well outside the line of breakers. These currents are ordinarily long and narrow, but in their outer zone they widen considerably. They extend out from a few hundred to about two thousand five hundred feet from the shore and vary from narrow belts 50 or 100 feet across in the feeders and neck to as much as 500 feet or more in the heads. Their velocity is known to be as great as two miles* an hour in some instances. This rate of flow is very inconstant, being greatly checked or even stopped by advancing wave fronts. The flow is capable of erosion near the shore where it produces channels a few feet deep. These channels may change in location and in form in periods of a day or even during the change of a tide.

There appear to be two principal locations where swimmers get into difficulties. The first and most common location of rescues is in the rip-current neck at the point where the large waves are breaking. A bather may find himself in this position either by slipping into a feeder channel which may be very near the shore, or by jumping through breakers in the zone next to the rip-current neck and being pulled gradually toward the neck until, having reached the main channel, he finds that he is in water beyond his depth. The solution for a swimmer caught in this situation is to try to swim out of the rip to the side opposite that from which he entered the neck. If he does not get out on one side, he should try the other. The second situa-

---

* The average velocity of a swimmer who swims 100 yards in 60 seconds is 5 feet per second or 3.4 miles per hour. To swim ashore against a rip current with a velocity of 2 miles per hour the swimmer would have to exceed a velocity of 2.9 feet per second or be able to swim 100 yards faster than 1 minute and 43 seconds.

tion of danger is beyond the breakers. A swimmer may have gone through the breakers in a rip current or may have swum into a rip while swimming along the coast outside of the breakers. Turning toward shore, he may find that he can make no progress. The current in the head is not ordinarily very strong, but most swimmers are not very fast. In some cases the rip is of short duration so that only a little patience is necessary; but at other times the rip, even if somewhat pulsatory, continues to move outward over a long period of time. The solution for a bather caught in this situation is to swim parallel to the shore and, after a relatively short distance, he will be helped by the laterally moving current of the rip. Then, after getting out of the turbulent rip, in coming landward he will be further assisted by the shoreward moving surface water next to the rip. While the local longshore currents play an important part in the development of rip currents, the close relationship shown between the rip development and the size of waves shows that the waves must be the dominant factor. The larger the waves, the more water is piled onto the shore and, therefore, the more water has to return seaward. However, the height and trend of the waves are largely responsible for the development of the local longshore currents so that these two factors are interrelated.

The writer's personal experiences as a lifeguard on the northern beaches of the Massachusetts coast are in close accord with the material presented above relative to rip currents and undertow.

Undertow. The term "undertow" is frequently used in connection with ocean swimming and bathing, and it is unfortunate that it has been used to describe a current that can draw a swimmer beneath the surface. Many people have been needlessly frightened by this inaccurate interpretation.

Sverdrup et al. (130) state: "The existence of undertow has not been satisfactorily explained, and is doubted by some observers." Bretz (19) is of the opinion that "water can't be piled upon a shore—it must flow down and back. The backflow beneath the waves out into deeper water is the undertow. Its velocity is generally overrated, for rarely do bottom slopes converge so as to concentrate it." Shepard et al. (118) make these statements:

The observation that floating objects are ordinarily carried out in the neck of a rip current only to the point where the larger waves break, while the rip itself is seen to extend well beyond the breakers, indicates that there must be a greater transfer of water outward beneath the surface than at the surface. On the other hand, it should not be supposed that this greater velocity just below the surface produces any appreciable tendency to draw a swimmer beneath the surface. Observations by writers, supported by information from lifeguards, show that, while a swimmer's body may be tilted by the subsurface flow, there is little if any tendency for it to be pulled under the surface. The common landward movement of floating objects and the rapid movement in that direction in the breakers show that the surface water over most of the area is moving landward. This motion may be compensated either by a return seaward in the form of undertow along the bottom or as a concentrated outward flow of surface and near-surface water in a rip current. The prevalence of rip currents shows that the return is largely by the second method. The reason for the dominance of the rip currents is that undertow is impeded by two factors. In the first place, there is more friction along the bottom so that outward flow is easier at the surface. Second, sea water is stratified to a certain extent with the heavier water underneath. As a result the light surface water cannot displace the water in this heavier zone.

Tidal Currents. Tidal currents present a hazard, but relatively few swimmers and bathers encounter them because most ocean swimming takes place along the open coast. Concerning tidal currents Sverdrup et al. (130) say: "Strong tidal currents through narrow sounds are readily accounted for by the fact that large amounts of water have to flow through these openings during each half tidal period. Tidal currents of 3.6 knots (1 knot equals 1.15 miles per hour) are not uncommon in sounds, and in many narrow straits tidal currents up to 10 knots or more occur at spring tides." Shepard et al. (118) state: "On the other hand, tide rips, which are actually due to the tide, are very pronounced along many of the narrow passages of the Maine coast."

Surf. In order to enjoy surf bathing with maximum safety, correct knowledge of the phenomena of waves and surf or breakers is essential. Waves are caused by the friction of winds that blow over the surface of the ocean. Waves that appear when no wind is blowing are known as rollers or ground swell. They are formed by high winds and have traveled many miles from their place of origin. Concerning wave action Bretz (19) says:

Wave motion does not involve an onward movement of the water. Only the form travels, the water goes round and round. This is true so long as waves are out in deep open water. If open-water waves approach a shore, they encounter shallow water and drag bottom. This causes them to travel more slowly. As the depth decreases less and less water is involved in the wave, though the energy remains essentially the same. This makes waves grow higher. When the decreasing depth is no more than the wave's height, the top part of the wave outruns the rest of it, the form becomes unstable, and the wave falls forward or "breaks." Orbital motion is completely destroyed and the water is thrown forward to advance as a horizontally flowing sheet against the shore. Thus the open-water waves of oscillation with orbital motion become waves of translation with only back-and-forth motion on the shore. On a low, gently sloping shore the waves may surge many feet beyond the average water line, only to flow back down the slope to meet the next wave of translation. Several waves of oscillation arrive and break while this is taking place, so the wave of translation is a compound effect and occurs at longer intervals (has a longer period) than do the waves of oscillation. With smaller waves or deeper water immediately offshore, breaking may not occur until the wave reaches the very shoreline, the place where its existence ends.

On long, gently shelving beaches surf riding is possible because the wave front is slowed down, but the outer portion of the wave continues to advance with great velocity (130) until the wave reaches shallower water and finally breaks.

Dawson (38) mentions a suspected hazard in surf bathing. He states: "It is the loss of specific gravity of aerated water. Hence the belief has been expressed that one important difficulty in swimming the rapids below Niagara is due to the churning up of the water and its consequent low density." This phenomenon was impressed upon the writer when he once attempted to swim across a shallow water area (during a storm) when the surf was particularly heavy. The most violent action on his part was necessary to extricate himself from this dangerous situation.

River Currents. River swimming is particularly dangerous when off-shore currents are present. According to Tarr and Von Engeln (133), "No river flows in a perfectly straight line. On the contrary, irregularities in the bed, a slumping down of one bank, and other causes turn the current toward one side, and cause the stream to cut first at one bank, then at the other." One should not attempt to swim against a current unless the current is weak and the swimmer is near shore. A swimmer caught in a strong current should utilize the force of the current by swimming diagonally across it even though he is carried far below the place where he intended to land.

Weeds and Kelp. Fresh-water weeds or salt-water eel grass are seldom encountered by the swimmer, but when encountered the swimmer should avoid making sharp, vigorous movements, which is his first instinctive reaction on contact. Instead, he should resort to slow, careful movements to prevent the weeds from entangling his arms and legs.

Concerning kelp Nicholls (90) states:

Any kelp which has broken loose by the force of the waves during a storm, or has broken loose by sand having infiltrated into the hold-fast and therefore breaking it loose, will float to the surface, and is held on the surface in a mass by the air sacks in the kelp. Thus, a swimmer endeavoring to swim over a kelp bed will become entangled in the leaves of this ocean forest. If the swimmer has training in underwater swimming he may safely swim in a kelp patch by submerging under the surface and swimming through the kelp trunks and coming to the surface for air, and then again submerging and swimming around in between the trunks and the kelp. This should not be tried by an amateur but only by expert ocean swimmers, and then only when a boat or paddle board is present to assist in case of trouble. A paddle board is an ideal craft to use in making a rescue in a kelp bed.

Other hints on swimming in kelp are as follows:

The modified crawl stroke with the head out, and with a slow arm stroke and practically no kick, is recommended as the best. The kelp with its air floats will hold the swimmer up as he passes over it. The habit of shaking off the kelp on each arm stroke should always be practiced. . . . There are records of the Coast Guard which show that seamen endeavoring to come ashore from a sunken fishing boat through a kelp bed, although wearing standard cork lifejackets, were drowned because kelp became entangled in the life-belt. Effective

water goggles are a great help in swimming in kelp beds.

WHEN TO SWIM

Swimming After Eating. Considerable misunderstanding is centered around how long one should wait after eating before going swimming. When to swim after eating is dependent upon such factors as skill, physical fitness, emotional feeling, and what and how much was eaten. The statement that one should wait one hour or two hours after eating before going swimming is not consistent with common practice and may cause needless apprehension. Today it is common practice for skilled swimmers to swim a few minutes after eating, but this should not be interpreted to mean that the unskilled swimmer should attempt a long, strenuous swim immediately after eating a heavy meal. Also, to believe that one should wait until the stomach is empty places unnecessary restriction on the swimmer. Best and Taylor (12) state: "After an ordinary mixed meal the human stomach empties within 3 to 4½ hours. A meal consisting of carbohydrates leaves more rapidly than one containing much meat and this more rapidly than one containing fat."

What and how much to eat is important if emotional tension is likely to be involved, such as is usually present preceding swimming competition, because emotional strain may interfere with digestion. Steinhaus* says: "We know that the emotions interfere with digestion much more than exercise." Karpovich (78) states: "As a rule, food should not be eaten three to four hours before a contest. The reason can be easily found if one attempts to swim, wrestle, run, and so on, on a full stomach. We must admit, however, that some athletes have made their records after eating a heavy meal close to the time of competition.

---

* Private communication.

These are exceptions which demonstrate that the human machine may perform well even under unfavorable conditions." To eat heavily just before a long, strenuous swim is not sensible because the distended stomach will cause respiratory interference. "The (12) diaphragm is the chief muscle of respiration, its movements being responsible during deep breathing for sixty per cent of the total amount of air breathed." Comparisons may be dangerous for the swimmer who forgets the significance of the skill factor in swimming and thinks only of how much and what was eaten by a friend who successfully completed a difficult swim soon after eating.

Concerning the effect of eating on the output of the healthy heart Best and Taylor (12) state: "Digestion of food causes an increase above the basal level of from thirty to forty per cent. This level is reached about one hour after the meal, persists for about three hours, and then gradually declines. The extra strain placed upon the diseased heart following a meal probably accounts for the attacks of angina pectoris which sometimes occur at this time. Ingestion of fluids also increases the cardiac output to a moderate degree. Both the cutaneous (skin) and splanchnic (internal) regions share in the increased blood flow." While this increase is not significant for the healthy heart, many people of middle age and older who enjoy swimming should follow a more conservative pattern than swimming within a few minutes after eating.

Morning Dip. The benefits accruing from a morning dip have been a subject of some discussion for years, but the weight of opinion now favors placing the morning dip on an optional basis for young and old. Pohndorf (94) states: "Before-breakfast dips should be on an optional basis and with adequate supervision. They should be dips, not swims." Bryant (2) is of the opinion "that the 'morning dips' should be made a matter of choice." Air and water temperature, reaction to cool water, preliminary warmup, and physical fitness are factors one should consider before experiencing a morning dip.

Reaction to Lightning. Flagg (49) says: "Each thunderstorm brings the question, where is the safest spot? It is dangerous to remain in an open boat, in an open field, on a beach, in bathing, or near a tree. The safest place is in a house, in an automobile, under a steel bridge, or if exposed, lying flat on the ground or sandy beach."

CRAMPS

All who swim or bathe should know that the pain and restriction of movement of a body segment associated with muscular cramp does not mean that drowning is imminent. Cramp does not cause a swimmer to be suddenly devoid of support or of the capacity to execute propulsive movements. Although the intensity of the cramp is greater or more likely to occur in some people than in others (12) it is unfortunate that the uninformed have placed so much emphasis on the menacing nature of cramp while swimming. Thomas (135), in his book which was published in 1904, states: "It is most unfortunate that almost every writer makes a terror of cramp. To cramp, for many years, has been attributed nearly every death in the water. Dr. Hunter Barron in 1886 says that the majority of the cases attributed to cramp have been due to failure of the heart's action resulting from exhaustion. The truth is, I believe, as Richardson says, that a person would not drown from cramp alone, but he might from panic brought on by fear of the effects of cramp." Cramp can be anticipated (82) and prevented or, if not, it should cause only temporary discomfort. Panic, which is the most dangerous by-product of cramp, may lead to hysteria, inefficient movements, and hyperventilation (12, 49), which tend to augment the cramp.

The parts of the body that are most commonly affected by cramp while swimming are the calf of the leg and the sole of the foot (2, 38, 82). Cramps in these segments accounted for 92 per cent of the cases reported in a study by Mason et al. with 6 per cent of the subjects reporting cramps. Lanoue (82) reports in a study of 1400 young men that 62 per cent of the cramps occurred in these two segments, with 4.5 per cent of the subjects reporting cramps. Silvia et al. report the same percentage based on a study of 350 young men who swam continuously for twenty-eight minutes with 2.3 per cent of the subjects reporting cramps. A cramp in some of the flexor muscles of the toes (sole of the foot) may result if the foot is held rigidly extended when flutter kicking, treading water, or scissors-kicking.

Many people have been needlessly frightened by stories of drownings attributed to stomach cramp. Lanoue (82) states that he questioned ten thousand boys and did not "encounter one first-hand observer, although there were a few second-hand, and a host of third-hand observers. In over 25 years' experience with swimming and swimming men, the writer has never seen one (stomach cramp) or seen a dependable swimming man who has seen one." Seaton (110) says: "Recent research tends to dispel the theory that stomach cramps are caused by swimming too soon after eating." The writer takes exception to the loose usage of the term "stomach cramp" when the term "abdominal cramp" is more adequate and accurate. Cases of abdominal cramp have been reported (110), but they have caused no more than passing inconvenience and have quickly responded to a change in position. The abdominal muscles do not compare in strength with the sacro-spinalis (back) muscles that extend the spinal column. A cramp of the adominal musculature, unless associated with a cramp of the iliopsoas (trunk flexors) muscles, which is in the realm of possibility, can be quickly stretched by extending the spinal column (38).

The cause of cramps while swimming is the subject of much debate. A possible cause is suggested by Best and Taylor (12), who state: "Alkalosis is also the apparent cause of tetany which results from increased pulmonary ventilation. In this case it is the excessive elimination of carbon dioxide which is the cause of the increased blood alkalinity. Collip has suggested that muscular 'cramps' which occur while swimming may be due to the hyperpnea (overbreathing) caused by the cold water." Flagg (49) is of the same opinion. "It is possible that the muscular cramps sometimes experienced during swimming are due to hyperventilation. This is caused by a combination of voluntary deep breathing and reflex deep breathing from exposure to cold water; sometimes too the element of fear is introduced." Dawson (38) says, "The tendency to pass into spasm (cramp) is increased: (1) by strong electrical stimuli, (2) by nervousness on the part of the subject, (3) by obstruction of the circulation, (4) by fatigue." Mason et al. (110) are of the opinion that "the factor which seems most predisposing to cramps occurring in a pool situation is fatigue of untrained muscles either before or during the swimming period." It is possible to conclude, therefore, that breath control, emotional control, avoidance of unusual muscle tension, and avoidance of undue fatigue for the untrained should receive important consideration when discussing the cause of muscular cramps while swimming.

The experience of Lanoue and Silvia et al. is that a cramp can be usually anticipated by the swimmer through the presence of a warning twinge. Lanoue

Fig. 25a. Cramp in the sole of the foot

or muscles) by moving into a tuck float, grasping the toes with one hand, and pulling the foot upward (flex foot) while the other hand is used to knead and massage the calf of the leg. When the swimmer heeds the premonitory (prodromal) twinge, stretching of the affected muscle or muscle group accompanied by a change of stroke is all that is necessary to prevent cramp. It is significant that, following instruction in this method, both Lanoue and Silvia did not find a case of cramp that forced the swimmer to the side of the pool for relief.

A cramp in the muscles of the sole of the foot can be released by pressing it against the instep of the other foot and extending the toes.

Fig. 25b. Cramp in the leg

says: "If the affected muscle is fully stretched immediately after the warning twinge, the total cramp will be less painful, and will disappear much sooner than if the traditional corrective procedures of rubbing and kneading are followed." Dawson (38) follows the same procedure of forcibly stretching the affected muscle. Lanoue found that anticipation and "stretching the affected muscle before it shortens eliminates practically all of the pain, and much of the probability of return." To stretch the affected muscle or muscle group the swimmer voluntarily contracts the antagonistic (opposite action) muscle group. In the case of a severe cramp in the calf of the leg (extensor muscles) the swimmer may assist the muscles on the front of the leg (flex-

A cramp in the extensor muscles of the ankle (calf of leg) can be released by flexing the ankle and vigorously rubbing the cramped area. This may be accomplished in a tuck float position or in the vertical float position.

How Much to Swim

Although interest here is principally in the safety factor of how much to swim, just where the safety factor begins and the health factor ends is a matter of conjecture. One who swims in cold water for fifteen minutes may endanger his health, and continued immersion may result in collapse and death by drowning. To set a definite length of time that is safe for everyone is, however, inadvisable. The only limit determinable is the time it takes for the appearance of such danger signs as a general feeling of discomfort, chilling, numbness, purplish hue of lips and fingernail beds, weakness, dizziness, and nausea. The well-conditioned long-distance swimmer, for example, can swim for several hours in water of 60° F. without any effect beyond a feeling of discomfort, but the ordinary swimmer would be foolhardy to extend his swimming time at such a temperature beyond thirty minutes.

Effect of Cold Water on Body Temperature. Taylor (134) states: "Cold water has a veritable appetite for heat. Man's loss of body heat during submersion for a period of twenty minutes at a temperature of 70° F. may be five times the normal basal rate. . . . The temperatures of 250 children under thirteen years of age were recorded both before and after they had been swimming for forty-five minutes in an indoor pool with the temperature of the water at 73° F. In only thirty, or twelve per cent, was a normal temperature maintained; in all the remaining 220 there was a reduction of temperature; in some the temperature fell as low as 95° F." Taylor's observations on a group of eight subjects who swam for forty-five minutes in ocean water at a temperature of 68.5° F. led him to conclude that "prolonged chilling produces peripheral vasoconstriction" [constriction of surface blood vessels], "peripheral stasis" [stoppage of surface blood vessels], and "anoxemia" [oxygen want].

Hypersensitiveness to Cold. Horton and Gabrielson (69) are of the opinion that "the number of people possessing hypersensitiveness [to cold] is not known, and those responsible for giving instruction in swimming should be familiar with the signs and symptoms of this condition." They state further that

. . . hypersensitiveness to cold is undoubtedly much more common than is indicated by the relatively few cases reported in the medical literature. The signs and symptoms may be classified as (1) local and (2) systemic. The local reactions are easily recognized: the skin exhibits a pallor during the period of exposure to cold and this is followed by redness, swelling, and increased temperature of the skin on removal of the exposed part from the cold. The skin also may exhibit urticaria or hives after exposure. After a latent period of from three to four minutes following the exposure, the systemic effects are manifested: There is a characteristic reaction which consists of a sharp decrease in blood pressure, and increase in pulse rate, a flushing of the face and a tendency toward, or the actual development of, syncope (fainting). The factors that seem to influence the local and systemic reactions are the length of the exposure and the temperature. If the water is cold the exposure need not be so long as would be necessary in warmer water. The important preventive measure is that people who are swimming should be aware of this condition and should begin to watch for its occurrence at public beaches. When people faint on the beach after having been in the water they should be examined for the signs and symptoms of hypersensitiveness to cold. Many times urticaria will appear in the region of the neck, arms, or legs. It must be remembered that this condition is not only the result of exposure to cold water, but also to cold atmospheric temperatures such as are found in the winter season. Some people are confronted with this condition as a result of proceeding from a hot atmospheric condition to an air-conditioned theater or other building in which there may be a draft. It is possible that people are more susceptible to this condition in the summer than in the winter; this may be because of the occurrence of natural desensitization of the subject in the water resulting from contact with gradual decreases in atmospheric temperatures.

Dawson (38) adds supporting evidence. The most disastrous symptom of an "athletic physician, attacked while bathing in a mountain lake, was intense weakness. In another case it was unconsciousness and in another vertigo (dizziness) and vomiting. One observer reports . . . several times while swimming there has been sudden weakness followed by collapse on shore; once the same thing happened as the result of a cold air bath." ˈ

Perforation of Ear Drum. Anyone who has a perforated ear drum (tympanic membrane) should not swim, because of the menace to health and safety, until the perforation has healed and permission to swim is granted by a physician. There is evidence (146) that cold water entering the internal ear (labyrinth) through a perforation in the ear drum may produce dizziness, vomiting, and the fall reaction. This may explain why some skilled swimmers have drowned under mysterious circumstances. Guttich produced the fall reaction on guinea pigs by paralyzing the labyrinth on one side by an injection of 5 per cent cocaine. The animals when placed in water would swim in a circle but were unable to swim straight, and after a short time would sink beneath the surface, where screwlike movements would begin that carried them downward to death by drowning.

Another serious reaction is vomiting. Food particles have been found repeatedly in the respiratory tracts and lungs of the drowned.

DISROBING

Knowledge of how to disrobe in the water is important to the swimmer and lifesaver alike, because water-soaked clothing interferes with swimming effi-

ciency and the shirt and trousers make very serviceable supports. There are times, of course, when disrobing is not necessary or desirable, such as when the shore is only a short distance away, when the water is cold, when some other effective support is available, or the approach swim is short and great urgency is necessary.

Occasionally the lifesaver may deem it advisable to disrobe before entering the water. His decision should be based on the apparent condition of the victim, the distance to be swum, and the kind of clothing he is wearing. Rapid disrobing, therefore, should be practiced by the lifesaver until he becomes proficient. The procedure followed by the Boy Scouts of America (17), called "How to Disrobe in Twenty Seconds," consists of the following steps:

1. Coat and shoes come off together
2. Trousers opened and dropped
3. Tie removed and shirt unbuttoned as trousers are kicked free
4. Shirt pulled back and down over left hand
5. Shirt sleeves stripped over right hand
6. Socks are skinned off feet, and
7. Undershirt over head
8. Ready to go

The body is supported in a horizontal stationary position by the alternate vertical action of the legs (Fig. 11), while

Fig. 26a. Removing jacket

both hands are engaged in removing the
jacket. Whether footwear is removed
first depends upon its type. Heavy boots,
for example, may be removed first, but
light footwear being less inconvenient
than the jacket, should be removed after
the jacket.

Fig. 26c.   Removing trousers

Fig. 26b.   Removing shoes

Before the tuck floating position is
assumed a maximum inspiration is taken
and both hands are used to remove one
shoe at a time. In the case of a non-
floater the free leg should be used to
provide some supporting action. Another
practicable method is to assume a back
floating position and use one hand to
remove the shoes while supporting the
body with the free hand and leg.

By alternate vertical action of the legs
the body is supported in a horizontal stationary position while both hands are
used to loosen and slide the trousers
down over the feet. The trousers are discarded only when the swimmer does not
need them as a support.

By alternate vertical action of the legs
the body is supported in a horizontal
stationary position while both hands are
used to remove the shirt. If a pull-over
garment is being worn it is pulled up to
the armpits, a vertical position is assumed, and the garment is grasped with
the arms crossed before pulling it off
over the head. The shirt is discarded
only when the swimmer does not need
it as a support.

Fig. 26d.   Removing shirt

Fig. 27a. Tying trouser legs together

the vertical or horizontal support position may be assumed, depending upon the swimmer's preference.

Of the various methods of inflating a pair of trousers the hand-plunging method offers the greatest adaptability (Fig. 33a). After the ends of the trouser legs have been tied together, the trousers are placed on the surface of the water, front downward. Then a right-handed swimmer holds, just beneath the surface, the top middle portion of the back of the trousers with his left hand. As the object of this technique is to force air under water and trap it in the trouser legs, the right hand starts its diagonal, downward, and forward movement from a point several inches above the surface of the water. The right hand action should finish several inches below the surface of the water, and under the left hand, so that the air forced under water will rise into the trouser legs. Brief practice will make it possible for the swimmer to trap enough air by two hand plunges to assure a serviceable support.

Trousers and Shirt as Supports

The discovery that the trousers and shirt can be used effectively as supports is not new (17), but the techniques have changed to some extent and those recommended here have been found by Lanoue et al. (84) and the writer to offer the greatest utility. Other techniques (17, 32), such as tying the trouser legs separately, tying the shirt sleeves separately, blowing air into the front of the shirt, and trapping air under the shirt can be used successfully.

Using the trousers as a support:

After the trousers have been removed the ends of the trouser legs should be tied together with a square knot. Either

Fig. 27b. Inflating trousers by hand plunging

Inflating trousers by flinging (See Fig. 27c):

In this method the trousers are placed over a shoulder, the top facing forward and the front facing downward. As the arms are lifted upward and swung forward, the top of the trousers is held securely, with the fingers inside. Bringing the open top of the trousers down

Fig. 27d. Inflating trousers by blowing

Fig. 27c. Inflating trousers by flinging

Otherwise the trousers cannot be lifted clear of the surface and insufficient air will be trapped to provide a suitable support.

Occasionally (Fig. 33c) this method is the only one practicable to replenish the air supply in a pair of partially deflated trousers. Since this method is used only when the top of the trousers is under water, it is necessary to submerge to blow air into them.

Fig. 27e. Trousers as a stationary support

quickly on the surface of the water will trap enough air to support several persons. During the lifting movement of the arms a vigorous treading action of the legs is necessary to prevent submerging.

Fig. 27f.   Trousers as a swimming support

Using Shirt as a Support:

After removing the shirt, tie the ends of the sleeves together with a square knot. Then inflate the left sleeve by blowing air into it through the top of the sleeve. As soon as this sleeve is full of air pinch off the top of the sleeve with the thumb and forefinger of the right hand and with the left hand move across the collar to the top of the right sleeve and inflate this sleeve by blowing. Of the various methods of inflating a shirt this method offers the greatest adaptability (Fig. 33c).

After the shirt sleeves have been inflated, the tops of the sleeves are pinched off, one in each hand, and the shirt is slipped over the head. The inflated shirt also can be used as a swimming support similar to the method employed with the trousers.

Fig. 28a.   Inflating shirt by blowing

After the trousers have been inflated the top is gathered together in one hand, the other hand being used to assist the process of slipping the head between the trouser legs. The top of the trousers is held under water with one or both hands, the swimmer using his legs for maneuvering purposes.

When body build and size of trousers permit, the head and arms can be slipped in between the legs of the trousers to make a serviceable swimming support. As air cannot escape from the trousers in this position, both hands are free for swimming. The trousers also can be used as a swimming support while on the back.

Fig. 29. Mill's bucket buoy
(Courtesy of George C. Adams)

OTHER SUPPORTS

Air trapped under such objects as a pail, number ten can, barracks bag, knapsack, steel helmet and helmet lining, pillow case, mattress cover, or nonporous hat converts them into effective supports.

Also such objects as an empty jug, two canteens tied together, several oars or paddles lashed together, pieces of buoyant debris, and a properly packed knapsack can be used effectively as supports.

The (18) air bucket buoy is a collapsible life preserver that can be carried around in the pocket, ready to be inflated if needed. In spite of the handy size, it will hold enough air to support anyone, even those who have no natural buoyancy. It is inflated simply by pulling it downward, from over the head into the water, and by holding it with the end open. It will hold air longer if it is soaking wet when inflated.

Fig. 28b. Shirt as a support

6.

Non-Swimming and Swimming Assists

NON-SWIMMING ASSISTS

Rescues close to shore can be accomplished by proper use of reaching and wading devices. The rescuer should observe measures to avoid being pulled into the water or thrown off balance. For instance, the rescuer should assume a well-braced position with center of gravity as near to his base of support as possible, and should maintain a firm grip on all extensions. The rescuer should also avoid over-reaching, and any sudden pulling action that will tear the extension out of the victim's grasp.

Reaching Assists:

From a properly balanced prone position with his upper trunk extended over the water, the rescuer reaches out his hand to the victim.

He could also use a pair of trousers as an extension.

From a firmly braced, crouched posi-

Fig. 30b. Extension assist from pool deck

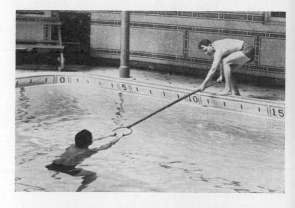

Fig. 30c. Pole assist from pool deck

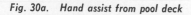

Fig. 30a. Hand assist from pool deck

tion the rescuer extends the reaching pole to the victim. The rescuer's grasp on the pole must be firm to prevent it from being pulled away by the victim's frantic action.

When the victim's head is under water and he is still conscious, he will in-

Fig. 30d. Hand assist from in water

stinctively seize the pole if it is held firmly against his body. The rescuer should be careful not to tear the pole out of the victim's hands while pulling him to safety.

The rescuer increases his reaching distance when extensions are not immediately available by jumping into the water, grasping the gutter with one hand, and reaching out with the other hand to the victim.

A human chain consisting of two or more rescuers using a hand-to-wrist grip can be used when other extensions are not available and the victim is too far out to be reached by a single rescuer. Or he could use a pair of trousers as an extension. The human chain also

Fig. 30e. Extension assist from in water

can be used with the anchor man firmly braced in shallow water.

Wading Assists:

Pole assist (See Fig. 31a)

From a firmly braced position in waist-deep water the rescuer extends the reaching pole to the victim.

Plank assist (See Fig. 31b)

From a position in waist-deep water the rescuer pushes a plank out to the victim.

SWIMMING ASSISTS

Swimming assists are used only when the swimmer is tired and able to follow instructions by the rescuer. Although a tired swimmer may not be immediately in danger of drowning, the rescuer should never forget that a tired swimmer may suddenly become panicky and attempt to seize him. The techniques included in the category of swimming assists are: clothing assists, novice assists, and the tired swimmer's carry.

Clothing Assists:

The rescuer is confronted with the necessity of supporting a tired swimmer for an extended period of time while awaiting rescue. The rescuer accomplishes this by removing his trousers and inflating them to provide a support for the tired swimmer. Then the rescuer removes the trousers worn by the tired swimmer and utilizes them as a support for himself. (See Fig. 32)

Fig. 31a. Pole assist

Fig. 31b. Plank assist

Fig. 33b.   Pulling trousers over feet

After inflating the trousers the rescuer assists the exhausted swimmer into a back floating position and then pulls the trousers over the exhausted swimmer's feet to a position around his chest.

Fig. 32.   Supporting tired swimmer

Fig. 33c.   Rescuer and exhausted swimmer supported by trousers and shirt

Fig. 33a.   Supporting exhausted swimmer and inflating trousers

The rescuer supports the exhausted swimmer with his left arm while he inflates the trousers by hand plunging.

The shirt is then inflated by blowing and pulled over the exhausted swimmer's feet to a position around his knees. The rescuer moves to a position beneath the exhausted swimmer where he is able to grip the trousers between his knees and provide support for himself and the exhausted swimmer's head. The rescuer is in position also to encircle the exhausted swimmer's chest with his arms and perform a rhythmic squeezing type of artificial respiration.

Fig. 33d. Towing exhausted swimmer

The rescuer grasps the trousers so that his forearm supports the exhausted swimmer's head and tows him in that position with the lifesaving stroke.

Fig. 35. Novice assist on back

The rescuer assists the novice who is swimming on his back by grasping him under the armpit so as not to interfere with the action of his arms and encourages him to keep swimming, while he provides the necessary support and propulsion with the lifesaving stroke. The rescuer's towing arm is held straight to avoid the tendency to lift the novice. For maximum efficiency the rescuer should swim directly in line with the novice.

Fig. 34. Novice assist on front

Fig. 36. Arm assist

Novice Assists:

The rescuer assists the novice who is swimming on his front by grasping him under the armpit so as not to interfere with the action of that arm, encourages him to keep swimming, while he provides the necessary support and propulsion with the lifesaving stroke.

The rescuer, after commanding the novice to grasp his wrist, grasps the novice's wrist with firm contact, and encourages him to keep kicking, while the rescuer provides the necessary support and propulsion with the lifesaving stroke.

Fig. 37.　Shoulder wrestling

Fig. 38a.　Approaching tired swimmer

When approaching a tired swimmer the rescuer should maintain some forward motion in a horizontal swimming position to assure a smooth "pick-up."

Fig. 38b.　Command: "Place your hands on my shoulders"

The rescuer should anticipate a sudden downward thrust by the tired swimmer and be ready to compensate by maintaining a high head-position and executing short and rapid breast-stroke movements. Some forward motion should be maintained by the rescuer during contact. Later, if necessary, the rescuer can instruct the tired swimmer to keep his elbows straight.

Tired Swimmer Assist:

Shoulder wrestling aids in preparing the rescuer for the vigorous supporting action that may be necessary upon the initial contact with the tired swimmer. The two participants assume a vertical support position, each with his hands on the shoulders of the other. On the command "Go" they attempt to submerge each other by pressing downward and attempting to move forward. The contest is terminated when one participant's head is forced beneath the surface.

Fig. 38c.　Command: "Head back"

This command places the tired swimmer in a more streamlined position, which is important during the initial stage of getting under way. Later the rescuer may instruct the tired swimmer to look him in the face, particularly if the water is choppy.

Fig. 38d. Command: "Wrap your legs around my body"

Close contact with the rescuer creates a feeling of security on the part of the tired swimmer. Greater mobility also is permitted when the tired swimmer uses his legs to maintain close contact with the rescuer. The use of the more conservative command, "Spread your legs," is called for when the rescuer lacks skill, physique, and confidence.

Fig. 38e. Position for executing a pivot turn

The rescuer instructs the tired swimmer to hold on tightly while he assumes a vertical support position and executes alternate turning movements with his arms.

A gradual swimming turn is easily accomplished after the rescuer instructs the tired swimmer to maintain a snug hold with his legs. This action by the tired swimmer frees the rescuer's arms to execute turning and propulsive movements.

Fig. 39. Defense against a panicky, tired swimmer

If the assist takes place a considerable distance from shore and the tired swimmer becomes panicky and attempts to grasp the rescuer, the latter should quickly place his hands on the tired swimmer's shoulders and exert sufficient force to prevent him from seizing his rescuer. The rescuer should continue to kick to maintain position, and without forcing the tired swimmer beneath the surface caution him to "take it easy." In case the rescuer decides he cannot cope with the situation he should quickly execute a two-hand block to move out of danger and then follow up with an appropriate approach.

When the distance to shore is short the rescuer may permit the panicky, tired swimmer to grasp him with a front head hold and body scissors. This type of assist is used frequently by experts (Fig. 60).

7.

Approaches and Tows

APPROACHES

The proficient rescuer is capable of contending with a wide variety of rescue situations. The rescuer who has just recently completed a lifesaving course should not, however, attempt to emulate the expert. Every rescuer should know the limitations of his skill, endurance, and emotional resources so that he will avoid becoming involved in a rescue situation that he cannot handle. Would-be rescuers who in turn need rescuing only complicate the task of the successful rescuer. One should recognize when a swimming rescue is beyond his capacity, and utilize some extension or support (Figs. 26b, 30e, 31b) which, while keeping him out of the clutches of a frantic victim, will enable him to help the victim to safety. Swimming rescues are most effective when limited to relatively short distances, and under such circumstances should take precedence over waiting for equipment that is not immediately available. A victim who appears to be in immediate danger of disappearing under water should be contacted as quickly as possible, and swimming is usually the quickest method of reaching a victim only a short distance away.

Although the rear approach is the safest approach, particularly when dealing with a struggling victim, there are occasions when the front surface approach should be used, especially if the expert rescuer judges that he can handle the victim without trouble and that further struggling is not only needless but may be overtaxing for the victim. The rescuer will find that most of those being rescued are co-operative and willing to do their utmost to follow the rescuer's instructions. There are occasions, however, when the rescuer may need to twist quickly away to avoid being seized by a frantic victim. Occasionally the rescuer may choose to use the front underwater approach when the struggling victim's head is above the surface and the clearness of the water permits adequate visibility.

Jump Entries:

Since the plunge entry (Fig. 1b) is fastest, it is generally used by the rescuer when taking off from the side of a pool, dock, float, or shore where the water depth is not less than three feet and bottom conditions are known to be safe. When the rescuer is in doubt concerning water depth, and the take-off height does not exceed three feet, a safer method is the stride jump. If he is suspicious of the presence of snags, submerged rocks, mud, or weeds, the rescuer should use a cautious wading or slide-in entry. For the stride-jump entry the rescuer takes off from one foot in a stride position with his arms raised sideward to shoulder level and his trunk angled forward about forty-five degrees. The position of the legs, arms, and trunk, and the forward angle of the

Fig. 39a. Stride jump

descent when a standing take-off is used, the rescuer should lean forward with his body straight, then step forward, bringing his legs together, and avoiding any bend-forward at the waist when looking downward. A tendency to rotate forward can be checked by lifting the knees, but a tendency to rotate backward originating from a jump take-off is much more difficult to control. If the drop is long it may result in landing on the back with consequent loss of consciousness and possible injury or death by drowning. Before making entry into the water the bent arms are clasped tightly across the chest, the knees are bent slightly, and the ankles are flexed to insure landing on the bottom of the feet. This type of entry provides maximum protection and control.

take-off, will prevent the rescuer from descending beneath the surface and will permit him to fix his eyes on the victim or spot where the victim was last seen.

Although a rescuer possessing skill and judgment may choose to dive from a greater height than ten feet, the majority of rescuers should jump rather than dive. The greater the height of the jump the greater the possibility of injury and the greater the need for skill and experience in jumping. The rescuer must be certain there is sufficient water depth and that bottom conditions are safe. A jump from a height of twenty feet into water twelve feet deep is safe for a skilled jumper when bottom conditions are firm, but if the bottom is soft there is danger of getting stuck. When sufficient water depth exists and bottom conditions are safe the height from which a rescuer can jump safely depends upon his ability to enter the water vertically. Although some adjustments are possible during the descent, the success of the jump depends largely upon the take-off. To insure a vertical

Fig. 39b. Compact jump

Fig. 40. Head up. Don't lose sight of
the victim

Fig. 41. Just before contact with victim

with such an energy-conserving stroke
as the breast stroke, side underarm
stroke, or side overarm stroke.

Approach Stroking:

During the approach swim the rescuer, regardless of the stroke used,
should fix his eyes on the victim or the
spot where he was last seen. The stroke
used most commonly is the crawl or
some modification of it, depending upon
the skill of the rescuer and the distance
to be swum. The rescuer should realize
the importance of conserving enough
energy for the tow to safety. He may,
therefore, decide to combine the crawl

The Reverse:

Before contacting a victim whose
head is above the surface, the rescuer
should execute a reverse by checking his
momentum with a sideward extension
and forward sweeping action of his
arms coincident with the "tucking" action of his legs. The reverse is important
as a safety precaution, and also to place
the rescuer in the most advantageous
position to overcome the inertia of the
stationary victim. However, if the victim's head is beneath the surface or
about to sink below the surface, the
rescuer may dispense with the reverse
and make contact immediately.

Fig. 42a. Armpit grasp

Fig. 42b. Moving into cross-chest tow

After several strokes by the rescuer to start the victim moving smoothly, the rescuer should turn onto his left side, maintain contact with the victim, and swing his right arm diagonally downward and across the victim's chest to the cross-chest position.

Fig. 43. Chin grasp

Rear Approach:

This technique may be employed with a struggling victim who might not react favorably to the chin grasp technique. The rescuer reverses directly behind the victim, where he is in position to grasp the victim's left armpit with his left hand or vice versa. As soon as contact is made the rescuer uses short, vigorous, lifesaving stroke movements to start the victim moving, concentrating on keeping his head above the surface. Immediately following contact the rescuer should speak sharply to the victim, instructing him to "take it easy," and providing enough upward force to permit the victim to keep his head out of water. Usually the victim will respond favorably to this supporting and propulsive action, and will co-operate to the extent of following the rescuer's instruction to "hold your head back," a position which facilitates "leveling." The rescuer may then decide to move into the cross-chest tow or to use this armpit tow. A victim who persists in struggling can be controlled, if desired, by placing him in the control tow.

With a passive victim the rescuer may elect to use the chin-grasp rear approach. To secure this hold, the rescuer reverses directly behind the victim until he is in position to grasp the victim's chin by extending his arm across the victim's shoulder, close to his neck. The rescuer should be careful to place the palm of his hand over the victim's chin and to avoid exerting pressure on his throat.

Coincident with getting under way the leveling process is accomplished by the rescuer who flexes (bends) his elbow to pull the victim's head back, using the victim's shoulder as a fulcrum and concentrating on keeping the victim's face above the surface of the water.

vigorous lifesaving stroke movements to get under way. Coincident with getting under way the rescuer turns the victim in preparation for a suitable tow, concentrating on keeping the victim's face above the surface.

Fig. 44b.   Moving into cross-chest tow

The victim is turned onto his back with a pulling action by the rescuer's right hand as the rescuer turns onto his right side and swings his left arm diagonally downward and across the victim's chest to the cross-chest position.

Fig. 44a.   Upper-arm grasp

Front Approach:

This technique enables the rescuer to cope successfully with a victim who has just disappeared under water and must be contacted as soon as possible and brought to the surface quickly. Valuable time may be lost groping for the victim's wrist when his upper arm is usually more accessible, particularly when the victim's arms are near his sides. The rescuer contacts the victim from above by reaching downward from the surface or employing a feet first surface-dive. The rescuer should grasp the victim's right upper arm near the shoulder with his right hand or vice versa. The victim is then brought vertically to the surface by the rescuer who employs

Fig. 45a.   Wrist grasp

When one or both of the victim's arms are accessible the rescuer reverses his direction and grasps the back of the victim's right wrist with his right hand or vice versa. When the victim's head is above the surface the rescuer should be ready to block any efforts on the part of the victim to seize him.

Fig. 45b. Moving into cross-chest tow

See explanation for Fig. 44b.

Fig. 46. Position for turn

Underwater Approach:

When the victim's face is above the surface and the water is clear the rescuer may choose to execute a quick vertical surface dive about six feet in front of the victim. This dive should carry him below the level of the victim's feet, at which point he levels off and

swims forward to position for the turn. The victim is turned by pushing with one hand placed at the front of one knee and pulling with the other hand placed behind the other knee. The rescuer then returns to the surface, being careful to support the victim's face above the surface without lifting him, by maintaining contact along his sides until one hand is placed under his armpit. The rescuer then gets under way and moves into an appropriate tow.

Fig. 47a. Possible result of close surface-dive

The rescuer is surface-diving too close to the victim, who grabs his legs and applies body scissors.

The rescuer, by executing vigorous breast-stroke arm movements, returns to the surface and causes the victim, if he continues to hold on, to be submerged. The rescuer is now in position to release the body scissors, after which he turns and works his legs free. Another effective procedure is for the rescuer to maintain his position until the victim tires and releases his hold.

Fig. 47b. Positions reversed

verted scissors kick. Although the control tow is limited to short distances, by it the skilled rescuer is able to control a struggling victim.

Fig. 48. Cross-chest tow

Tows

By being proficient in the use of several tows the rescuer has a choice of several methods with which to meet various kinds of rescue needs. For maximum efficiency the rescuer should know the principal advantages and disadvantages of each tow. The cross-chest tow provides excellent control and support of the victim and is usually the most satisfactory all-round tow, but since most rescuers find it tiring over long distances, it can be combined with easier tows, such as the armpit tow, hair tow, or collar tow. The hair tow is well adapted for longer distances, but is limited to a passive victim whose hair is long enough to permit a firm grasp. The armpit tow is efficient over longer distances and in rough water, but as the rescuer has limited control it is not acceptable for use with a struggling victim. It is evident that the collar tow is limited to use with a victim who is wearing a shirt or coat. The head tow is very tiring for most rescuers, but is acceptable to those who possess a powerful inverted breast-stroke kick or in-

This tow is most commonly used because it provides good support and a sense of security for the victim, and enables the rescuer to control most struggling victims. Its disadvantage is that the victim is directly over the rescuer and a heavy victim will interfere with the rescuer's leg action. In long tows it is advisable for the rescuer to move to the side of the victim or change to the hair tow or armpit tow.

The best position for the victim is directly over the side of the rescuer's body. In this way he is held in position by the rescuer's arm, which is placed over the victim's shoulder and across his chest until the rescuer's hand is in contact with the victim's side just below the armpit. The victim's shoulder is in close contact with the rescuer's armpit, and the victim is held in a firm, snug grip but without undue pressure. The rescuer should be careful that his upper arm does not cause pressure against the victim's neck, and he should exercise care that the victim's face is above the surface at all times.

Fig. 49. Control tow

To control a violently struggling victim over a short distance, the rescuer should grasp the wrist of the arm that is across the victim's chest with his free hand and pull forcefully until his hand and wrist are under the victim's armpit. This action will cause the arm across the victim's chest to tighten and prevent him from twisting away. The rescuer continues to use the scissors kick for propulsion and support.

Fig. 50. Hair tow

The rescuer may elect to use the hair tow with a passive victim when the water is smooth and a long tow is necessary. He should maintain contact with the victim while moving into the tow (Figs. 42b, 44b) which consists of placing the palm of the hand on top of the victim's head, with the fingers par-

tially spread, and sliding the hand toward the forehead, where he flexes (hooks) his fingers and thumb into the hair. To place the towing arm in a position parallel to the surface, the rescuer extends (depresses) his wrist, exercising care to keep the victim's face above the surface. The towing arm should be straight but not rigid to insure a smooth tow.

Fig. 51. Head tow

The rescuer who possesses a strong inverted breast-stroke kick or inverted scissors kick may choose to use the head tow while towing the passive victim. The leg action, however, must be speeded up to maintain proper support and propulsion, for which reason this tow is too fatiguing for most rescuers. The rescuer is directly beneath the victim in a half-sitting position which places the legs out of contact with the victim's body. His arms are straight without being tense, and the hands are placed on each side of the victim's face with the palms of the hands over the victim's ears, the thumbs over his temples, and the middle fingers along the line of his jaw. The hold should be firm but the rescuer should avoid any tendency to exert pressure against the victim's throat.

Fig. 52.   Collar tow

Fig. 53.   Armpit tow

This tow is the same as the hair tow except that the rescuer tows the victim by the collar. Although it has only limited use, this tow is effective when towing a conscious victim in rough water because it permits him to lift his head and adds to his sense of security by preventing water from dashing over his face and up his nose. When towing an unconscious victim, the rescuer's forearm serves as a support for his head.

The armpit tow is the novice assist on back (Fig. 35) adapted to serve as a carry for the passive victim who does not have sufficient hair to permit using the hair tow. Also it is a very effective rough-water tow for a conscious victim who can lift his head, since it adds to his sense of security by preventing water from dashing over his face and up his nose. This freedom of movement is not possible when the victim's head is immobilized by the hair tow or head tow.

When a near double-drowning occurs close to shore the rescuer should make a vigorous effort to tow both victims to shallow water by employing the hair tow or armpit tow.

Fig. 54.   Towing two persons

8.

Defensive Tactics, Releases, and Water-Wrestling

DEFENSIVE TACTICS

Most swimming rescues consist of an approach, a tow, and subsequent treatment for shock. Circumstances may arise, however, when the rescuer will need to have a knowledge of defensive tactics in order to avoid the grasp of a frantic drowning person. These circumstances may occur during a front approach, during an approach to a tired swimmer, or following the sudden overturning of a small craft. Knowledge of defensive tactics will enable the rescuer to protect himself during such emergencies, with confidence and dispatch. Training in defensive tactics teaches the prospective rescuer the value of speed and aggressiveness. When avoiding the clutches of a frantically struggling person, unless he acts quickly and powerfully, the rescuer may find himself confronted with the much more serious problem of effecting a release. If the rescuer has to employ a defensive tactic as a purely defensive measure due to the size and strength of the victim, he should break away in order to determine the best follow-up procedure.

The rescuer should be skilled in the execution of the two-hand block and foot block, pivot parry, and rear pivot breakaway. Although he may never need these techniques, the rescuer who has acquired them is well equipped to protect himself in all situations.

Fig. 55a. Ready position

Two-Hand Block and Foot Block:

If the rescuer should find himself just within the reach of the frantic victim who attempts to seize him, he may choose to block the victim's efforts with his hands and forearms while looking for an opening to execute a front approach followed quickly by the control carry. Diligent practice in this technique is important because it helps to develop agility, anticipation of movements, and aggressiveness in the rescuer.

If the rescuer should misjudge his distance when about to execute a front approach and find himself about to be seized by the frantic victim, he can block the victim's efforts by pushing vigorously against the upper part of the victim's chest or face with both hands,

Fig. 55b. Block with head up

victim's chest. This action should be followed immediately by the foot-block position.

Fig. 55d. Position for foot block

simultaneously or alternately. This pushing action, which will cause the rescuer to move backward out of the reach of the victim, should be quickly followed by the movement of one foot into position (Fig. 55d) to ward off any further seizure by the victim. When the blocking action takes place above the surface and on the same plane as the victim the rescuer should keep his head up for better vision.

The rescuer has just completed the two-hand block and is now in position to use his foot to ward off further efforts by the victim to seize him. The rescuer should be careful not to kick the victim while blocking him on the upper part of his chest. If the victim should grasp his foot the rescuer may choose to use his other foot to effect a release by pushing against the victim's shoulder, or he may submerge the victim by straightening the leg (extending hip), moving into a vertical position, and maintaining contact with the hands on

Fig. 55c. Block with head down

If the victim encircles the rescuer's head with his arms or if he is on a higher plane than the rescuer, the latter should quickly "duck" (flex neck) his head without sinking vertically and simultaneously employ a vigorous pushing action against the upper part of the

Fig. 56a. Head turn

the victim's head or shoulders while remaining above the surface. The rescuer will be in position to move into the control carry as soon as the victim releases his hold or is forced to do so by the thrusting action of the rescuer's free leg against the victim's shoulder.

Rear Pivot Breakaway:

If the rescuer should be attacked from the rear by a frantic victim he should rotate (twist) his head sharply downward to the right or left, co-ordinated with a quick 180-degree twist (half twist) with his shoulders in the same direction. This will enable him to face the victim and thus be in position to complete the "breakaway" by pushing vigorously against the victim's chest (Fig. 56b). The downward rotating movement of the rescuer's head must be the initial movement so as to prevent the victim from seizing the rescuer's head and exerting pressure against his throat. A twisting action of the shoulders to the left can be assisted by a vigorous backward action of the left elbow co-ordinated with a forward action of the right arm across the chest. This action of the arms is reversed when the shoulder twist is to the right.

and is pushing against the victim's chest to complete the technique. As the rescuer's head is down the victim's encircling arms will slide off over the back of his head. The breakaway should not be considered completed until the foot-block position is assumed (Fig. 55d).

Fig. 57a. Contact

Fig. 56b. Push-away

The rescuer has completed the twisting action with his head and shoulders

Front Parry:

When either the rescuer or victim or both move toward each other, the rescuer may find the front parry more effective than the two-hand block. Forward movement, which may be caused by a current, wave, frantic action, or swimming action, can be utilized by the rescuer to move quickly to the rear of the victim and secure him in the control tow. The rescuer should make contact with the victim by driving his hands sharply upward under the victim's shoulders to lift him slightly, coincident with ducking (flexing neck) the head so as to cause the victim's arms to slide over the back of the head.

Fig. 57b.   The lift

The rescuer is lifting the victim and pulling him forward. At the same time the rescuer is moving under the victim's shoulder to the rear where he emerges to secure the victim in a control tow.

RELEASES

A rescuer called upon to perform a swimming rescue is always confronted with the possibility that a frantic drowning person may secure a tight hold on his head, arms, or body. Although a rescuer constantly aware of this danger seldom finds it necessary to use a release technique, if he is trained in release methods he is prepared to meet any eventuality. While learning the release techniques, the rescuer should at all times be cognizant of the importance of breath control, water agility, and aggressiveness. Watermanship is based on these three fundamentals and no one can be considered

proficient in the water unless he can demonstrate mastery of all of them.

The basic release methods are: release from the double grip on one arm or wrist, release from the front head hold with or without body scissors, and release from the rear head hold. No rescuer should ever permit himself to be seized with a rear head hold and body scissors because to the writer's knowledge no release for this hold exists (Fig. 67). During his training period the rescuer will find that when the victim exceeds him in size, strength, and breath control all release methods have limitations.

Release techniques should always incorporate the principles of correct body position, effective leverage, quick, powerful reaction, and breath control. The effectiveness of the release methods are based on an understanding and proper execution of these principles.

Release for Double Grip on One Arm:

The arm assist (Fig. 36), attempted front surface approach, or recovery of submerged victim may result in a double grip on one arm or wrist that must be

Fig. 58a.   The grip

Fig. 58b.   Control position

Fig. 59a.   Moving into position

released. The victim has seized the rescuer with a double grip on the right arm and the rescuer is in position to start the release.

As the rescuer pulls the victim toward him with his right arm, he vigorously swings his left arm down and around the back of the victim's neck until his hand is in contact with the victim's chin. Coincident with this action the rescuer executes a powerful leg drive that raises him above the victim and enables him to submerge the victim. In this position the rescuer may find it possible to pull his arm free of the victim's grasp, since the victim may release the hold because he has been forced under water. Or the rescuer may keep the victim under water until the latter releases his hold. The rescuer will

then move quickly into the control tow, crossing the victim's chest with either the right or left arm.

Release for Front Head Hold and Body Scissors:

Although it is unusual for the victim to seize a rescuer in a front head hold and body scissors, the tired swimmer being assisted in the tired swimmer's tow may become frantic and seize the rescuer in this manner. During the initial phase of the release the rescuer should keep his head up and execute strong breast-stroke movements so as to maintain a horizontal swimming position and at the same time remain above the surface and stay above or on the same plane as the victim. The rescuer should never permit a victim to seize him in a front head hold and body scissors so that his face is in contact with the victim's chest. Even when the rescuer is as strong or stronger than the victim he will experience great difficulty in effecting a release if caught in this position and may be unable to do so without the assistance of another rescuer.

The rescuer reaches up quickly with both hands to grasp the hair on the front of the victim's head while he continues to hold his own head back and

Fig. 59b.   Head snap-back, head-hold release

a sharp upward push against the victim's arms coincident with ducking (flexing neck) his head, thus causing the victim's arms to slide over the back of the rescuer's head.

Fig. 59c.   Control position, body-scissors release

to execute vigorously the breast-stroke kick or scissors kick to maintain position and some forward motion. If the victim does not have sufficient hair to permit a firm grasp, the rescuer should place one hand over the victim's forehead and the other hand over his mouth in preparation for the snap-back. To execute this release the rescuer "snaps" the victim's head back under water by exerting a vigorous downward pull. The combined effect of the pain associated with pulling on the hair plus the hyperextended (bent) position of the victim's neck and the forcing of his face under water, thus interfering with his breathing, will cause the victim to release his hold. The rescuer should exert maximum effort only when his own life is in danger, because in such a release it is possible to cause serious injury to the victim.

When practicing this release remember that violent action can result in injury to the victim's neck. When practicing with a victim who has sufficient breath control and strength to maintain the head hold even after his head has been forced back under water, the rescuer should quickly move his hands from the victim's face or hair to exert

As soon as the head hold has been released the rescuer should move his hands to the victim's shoulders and exert sufficient force to keep the victim submerged so as to prevent him from seizing the rescuer again. The rescuer should hold his own head above the surface so as to permit breathing and should continue to execute the breast-stroke kick or scissors kick to maintain his position and forward motion. The rescuer should continue to hold the victim in a submerged position unitl the body-scissors hold is released.

After the release has been completed and while the victim is still submerged, the rescuer should move forward and to the rear of the victim, so as to secure a control tow by placing either his right or left arm across the victim's chest.

When effecting the front head hold and body scissors release the rescuer should avoid the vertical position because of the increased difficulty in that position of forcing the victim's head under water while staying above the surface oneself. Moreover the rescuer

Fig. 59d.   Moving into control tow

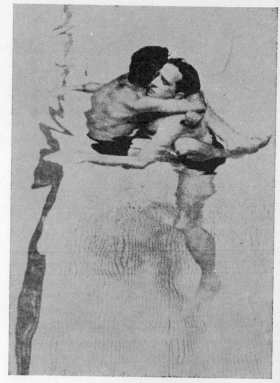

Fig. 60.   Confidence support

who learns and practices supporting a victim while in the vertical position will have acquired increased confidence and endurance.

Release for Front Head Hold:

If the two-hand block (Fig. 55c) does not enable the rescuer to break free from the frantic victim's grasp, the rescuer will have to resort to the front head-hold release. Since the rescuer has ducked his head trying to break free, the only part of the head which the drowning person seizes is the back. It is important that the rescuer avoid being seized with his head up because of the strain that will be placed on his neck when he executes the push-way and the increased difficulty he will encounter in pushing the victim's arms off his head. As soon as he realizes that he cannot break free, the rescuer places his hands on the victim's hips to start the push-

Fig. 61.   Push-away

away and prevent the victim from applying the body scissors. This push-away by the rescuer against the victim's hips will break the security of the victim's hold by forcing his body into a horizontal plane. If the push-away does not cause the victim to release his hold the rescuer quickly moves his hands to the victim's elbows and there exerts a vigorous upward push to complete the release (Fig. 62c). The rescuer then moves forward under one of the victim's arms, remaining in close contact to prevent the person being rescued from turning around and again seizing him. The rescuer then continues into the control tow (Fig. 62d).

Fig. 62b.   Push-away

Release for Rear Head Hold:

When the rear pivot breakaway does not enable the rescuer to get free of the frantic victim's grasp, the rescuer will have to resort to the rear pivot release. In attempting to break away before the victim can secure a hold, the rescuer should rotate his head to the left or right. This movement is a safeguard against any possibility of the victim exerting pressure against the rescuer's throat, and it also permits the rescuer to complete a pivot without undue strain on his neck. The rescuer's hands should be in

position to prevent the victim from seizing him with the body scissors while he executes the pivot.

To execute the pivot the rescuer drops his left shoulder, at the same time driving his left elbow vigorously backward and crossing his right arm close to his chest coincident with rotation (twisting) of his trunk to the left. Even when he cannot move his head in the tight grasp of the victim's arms, the rescuer can move his body to a position where he can employ the push-away release (Fig. 61).

Fig. 62a.   Head turn

Fig. 62c.   Head release

After loosening the victim's hold by pushing his body into a horizontal position the rescuer quickly moves his hands to the victim's elbows where he exerts a

Fig. 62d. *Moving into control tow*

Fig. 62e. *Head-lock somersault release*

vigorous upward push to complete the release. The rescuer then moves forward under one of the victim's arms, remaining close to the victim's body to prevent him from turning around to seize the rescuer again.

The rescuer now reaches across the victim's back to his opposite shoulder, all the time maintaining contact with the victim's body with his right arm. As the rescuer emerges he continues to move to the rear of the victim where he completes the control tow (Fig. 49).

He may choose the head-lock somersault release instead of the technique just described (Figs. 62a, b, c, d). After a right pivot the rescuer grasps the victim by the hair or face with his right hand while he slides his left arm under the victim's legs. Coincident with forcing the victim's face under water the rescuer lifts the victim's legs to cause him to execute a back somersault which is usually sufficient to obtain release from the hold. Continued forcing pressure against the victim's face will cause the victim to rotate into the underarm strangle (Fig. 64), which is used only during watermanship training. The rescuer can increase his effectiveness against the stub-

Fig. 63. *In position for release*

born victim by using both hands to force the victim's head back. The rescuer should exercise caution when employing this release with an unsuspecting victim because of the considerable force that he can exert to snap the victim's head back.

Assisting Would-Be Rescuer:

Occasionally a would-be rescuer is seized by a frantic victim who will cause both to drown unless rescue arrives soon. When the distance to shore is too far for a double tow (Fig. 54) the rescuer swims to the rear of the first victim, grasps him by the chin with both hands, and places one leg over one of the victim's shoulders so that his foot is in contact with the victim's arms encircling the would-be rescuer's neck. The rescuer separates the two by pushing strongly against the victim's arms as he pulls against the victim's chin. This action combined with the frantic efforts of the would-be rescuer to free himself will cause the victim to release his hold on the would-be rescuer's head. Release from a body scissors is obtained by keeping the victim submerged and assisting the would-be rescuer to stay above the surface until the victim's hold loosens and the would-be rescuer can twist away. Before proceeding to safety with the victim, the rescuer may consider it advisable to instruct the would-be rescuer to rest before attempting the return swim. The rescuer should not forget, however, that the would-be rescuer may be so fatigued that he too will need assistance. If the victims are children or small adults, the expert rescuer possessing a strong, inverted breast-stroke kick or inverted scissors kick may decide to carry both victims to safety with the double armpit tow by grasping each victim under the armpit. Of course, if another rescuer is at hand, or if the victim carried to safety is conscious, the first or second rescuer should go to the assistance of the would-be rescuer or second victim.

WATER-WRESTLING

Water-wrestling serves as an excellent conditioner, as well as a constant reminder of the importance of breath control, agility, aggressiveness, and emotional control in rescue situations. Rules are necessary, however, to produce the desired results. These rules are:

1. Match consists of two out of three falls.
2. Fall occurs when opponent is held securely with the control tow with or without body scissors (Fig. 65), judo strangle (Fig. 66), underarm strangle (Fig. 64), regular strangle with or without body scissors (Fig. 67), or is tired out within the thirty- to sixty-second time limit.
3. Either wrestler may acknowledge a fall by ceasing to resist.
4. Wrestling is confined to a circle ten feet in diameter. Failure to remain in circle is penalized by loss of a fall.
5. Referee's position is a double grip on the opponent's arm (Fig. 58a). Grip must be maintained until opponent makes contact, after which both wrestlers attempt to secure a pinning hold or to tire out opponent.
6. Referee starts each contest with command, "Wrestle!"
7. Rest period of one minute between falls.
8. If a match requires three falls, the referee's position for the last fall, which gives the advantage to the wrestler whose arm is held, is decided by choosing.

Three precautionary measures should be observed by both wrestlers:

1. Fingernails should be trimmed to prevent scratching.

Fig. 64. Underarm strangle

2. Striking opponent's ears is barred since this may cause rupture of the ear drums (tympani).

3. *Strong* pressure across opponent's throat is barred since this may cause unconsciousness or injury.

Pinning Holds:

As wrestler A submerges wrestler B, he moves forward quickly and encircles wrestler B's neck, so that the back of wrestler B's head is under his armpit and his forearm is across wrestler B's throat. Wrestler A then grasps the wrist of the arm which is across wrestler B's throat with his other hand and exerts sufficient force to prevent wrestler B from twisting away. Wrestler A releases wrestler B as soon as he ceases to resist.

Wrestler A holds wrestler B under water as he moves to the rear of wrestler B to secure him in the control carry (Fig. 49) and body-scissors hold. Sufficient force is exerted by wrestler A to prevent wrestler B from twisting away.

Fig. 65. Control tow and body scissors

Fig. 66. Judo strangle

Fig. 67. Double stretch

Wrestler A first secures wrestler B in the control tow and then quickly slides the arm that was across wrestler B's chest upward across wrestler B's throat, coincident with grasping the free arm just above the inside of the elbow. The free hand is then placed against the back of wrestler B's head and forward pressure is exerted which forces wrestler B's head under water and causes pressure against his throat. Wrestler A must be careful to exert controlled pressure or wrestler B may lose consciousness.

Wrestler A quickly swings one arm around wrestler B's neck until he contacts wrestler B's throat with the bend of his elbow. Coincident with grasping the wrist of this arm with his free hand wrestler A applies body scissors. The double stretch occurs when wrestler A tightens the body scissors and exerts backward pressure with the neck strangle. Wrestler A must be careful to exert controlled force to avoid causing injury to wrestler B. (The neck strangle without body scissors is an effective pinning hold.)

9.

Equipment Rescue

SHOULDER LOOP AND LINE

The rescuer who is skilled in the use of rescue equipment is prepared to act effectively when an equipment rescue situation arises.

One of the least involved equipment rescue methods entails the use of a light line with a shoulder loop tied at the leading end. This method requires a rescuer who swims to the aid of the victim and an assistant who is responsible for playing out the line and hauling both victim and rescuer ashore. The assistant must be an individual who will not become panicky if he has to wade out into the water or surf. When the assistant is in the water he should start hauling in the rescuer and victim by grasping the line firmly, and quickly returning to shore where he completes bringing the rescuer and victim ashore by hauling in on the line hand-over-hand. The assistant should watch the rescuer and victim carefully while pulling them through the breakers. Misjudging the force of a breaker may cause the rescuer to lose his grasp on the victim and complicate the rescue.

The rescuer places the shoulder loop over one shoulder and under the opposite arm while his assistant holds the coiled line in readiness to play it out. The rescuer then executes a head-up plunge or stride-jump entry (Fig. 39a).

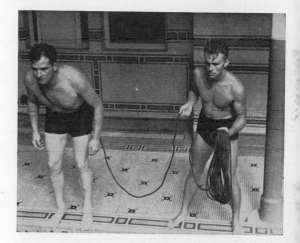

Fig. 68a. Ready position

Fig. 68b. Approach

Regardless of the stroke used during the approach the swimmer should fix his eyes on the victim or upon the spot where he was last seen.

If advisable, the rescuer reverses direction, and when one of the victim's wrists is available employs the wrist-grasp front approach (Fig. 45a). Otherwise he uses the most appropriate approach.

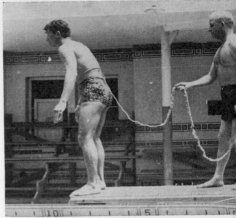

Fig. 69.   Chain line (Courtesy of G. C. Adams)

Fig. 68c.   Tow

Coincident with getting under way, the rescuer turns the victim onto his back by a vigorous pulling and turning action employing several vigorous lifesaving stroke movements. The rescuer then moves into the cross-chest tow (Fig. 48) and grasps the line securely with his free hand in preparation to being pulled ashore by his assistant. The assistant should maintain a slight tension on the line to prevent the rescuer from becoming entangled in it, but should not start the hauling-in process until he sees that the rescuer has a secure grasp of the line. If possible, the rescuer should have the shoulder loop under his left arm when using a left-arm cross-chest tow (or vice versa) to prevent possible injury because of undue pressure across his neck in case his grasp on the line is lost or his assistants are over-zealous.

The Boy Scouts of America use the chain rescue line as one of their defense

measures to protect a troop swimming party:

The line used should be two fifty foot lengths of No. 5 sash cord, which is slightly less than one-fourth inch in diameter. By using continuous chain knots these lengths can be reduced to about ten feet. The running end (running ends should be colored or given some other distinctive marking) of the first rope should be fastened to the fast end of the second. The running end of the second rope will then be pulled out and a loop about fifteen inches long formed in its end. (Use a bowline or an overhand knot on a bight.) This loop is placed over one shoulder and under the opposite arm of the rescue member of the team. Should it become necessary for him to enter the water to give assistance, he will make a running or a jump entry. As he does so, the rope will play out behind him. His partner will pull him in, as he holds his man with one hand and grasps the line with the other. (18)

RING BUOY

This type of rescue equipment is found frequently on the water front and the lifesaver should be familiar with its use. The ring buoy can be thrown with or without a line attached, or used with a shoulder loop and line. When used with

Fig. 70. Underhand delivery

a shoulder loop and line the rescue procedure is essentially the same as described under shoulder loop and line.

Throwing the Ring Buoy:

The rescuer, if he is right handed, stands in a slightly crouched position with his left foot forward. When throwing a ring buoy without a line attached, he should fix his eyes on a spot just within reach of the victim's hands or, to increase the chances of success, a few feet behind the victim. When the ring buoy with a line attached is used (most common), the rescuer drops the unattached end of the line to the ground, places his left foot on the line next to the lemon (Fig. 73), and holds the coiled line loosely in his left hand. The ring buoy is held on the inside rim and is thrown with a vertical under-hand motion. A side-arm motion will be found necessary, however, if the rescuer is standing against a railing. Most rescuers can throw a ring buoy accurately for about fifty feet without hitting the victim, and this distance can be exceeded by the more skillful. Allowances for wind

and water currents are necessary if maximum accuracy is to be obtained. While hauling the victim to safety the rescuer should employ a steady hand-over-hand pulling action to avoid tearing the ring buoy from the victim's grasp. As soon as the victim has been pulled to safety the rescuer should give him immediate assistance.

TORPEDO BUOY

The piece of lifesaving equipment best adapted to surf rescue is the torpedo buoy. For the victim who is not too far from shore, the torpedo buoy is most effective when used with a line attached. However, when the distance to the victim exceeds the length of the line, the rescuer

Fig. 71a. Ready

should detach the line and carry out the rescue with the torpedo alone. (Occasionally, the torpedo buoy is used to support several victims while awaiting the arrival of a lifeboat.) Only a rescuer who is familiar with shore, surf, and water conditions is equipped to act with maximum efficiency.

The rescuer places the shoulder loop over one shoulder and under the opposite arm and holds the torpedo buoy in a horizontal position by one of the side lines while moving into position to execute a plunge entry or a stride-jump entry.

Fig. 71c.   Approach

Fig. 71b.   Take-off

When entering known waters the rescuer executes a standing or running plunge entry (Fig. 1b) coincident with releasing the torpedo buoy. Regardless of stroke used during the approach swim, the rescuer should fix his eyes on the victim, or upon the spot where he was last seen.

Fig. 71d.   Return

When the rescuer reaches a point about three feet ahead of the victim, he pulls the trailing torpedo buoy forward and presents to the victim the end opposite that to which the shoulder loop is attached, with instructions to reach forward and grasp the forward part of the buoy. The victim in the illustration is in the process of reaching forward.

The rescuer may use the breast stroke, the side-underarm stroke or the side-overarm stroke to tow the victim to safety. These strokes provide a strong propulsive action without undue fatigue to the rescuer and allow him both to observe how the victim is faring and to watch surf and current conditions.

about thigh depth, holding the line over his head and letting it slide through his hands. Later he helps the reel man to haul the rescuer and victim to shore.

Fig. 72b.   Return

Fig. 72a.   Ready

Torpedo Buoy and Reel (Courtesy of G. C. Adams):

The more efficient method of using the torpedo buoy is with a reel and line. The take-off and approach do not differ from the procedure followed when the torpedo buoy is used alone, except that the leading end of the torpedo buoy is presented to the victim instead of the opposite end. When another assistant is available he helps to reduce the drag of the line in the water during the approach swim by entering the water to

The rescuer presents the torpedo buoy to the victim, instructs him to seize the side lines, moves to the rear without removing the shoulder loop, and supports the victim by reaching under his arms to grasp the side lines in preparation to being hauled ashore, hand-over-hand, by the reel man. The reel man and his assistants must be careful to exert a steady, powerful pull so as to avoid tearing the torpedo buoy from the grasp of the rescuer and victim. When dealing with a helpless victim the rescuer should employ the most appropriate approach and cross-chest tow (Figs. 68a, 68b, 68c).

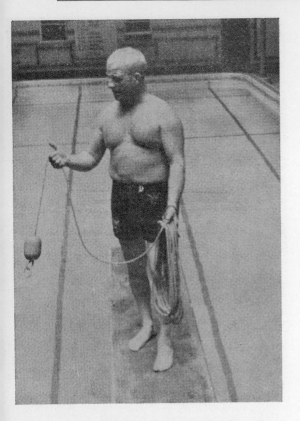

Fig. 73.   Position for throwing

Heaving Line (Courtesy of G. C. Adams):

The throwing end of this type of heaving line is weighted with a metal ring and a wooden lemon. When the rescuer is in position for the throw he stands in a slightly crouched position with his left foot forward, the throwing end of the line in his right, the coiled line held loosely in his left hand with the fast end looped around the left wrist. The throwing end is then swung several times in a vertical, clockwise circle. When sufficient speed of whirling has been reached, which depends upon the distance to be thrown, the line is released. The rescuer should fix his eyes on a spot beyond the victim to increase the chances of success and to avoid hitting the victim. For most

rescuers accuracy is possible over a distance of about fifty feet, although this distance may be exceeded by the more skillful.

SURFBOARD

Although the surfboard is not so stable as a lifeboat, it is favored by many rescuers because it can be quickly and easily launched, can be propelled much faster than the rescuer can swim or row a boat, and has sufficient bouyancy to support the rescuer and victim on its deck, or to support a rescuer and several tired swimmers clinging to its sides. The effective use of the surfboard is dependent upon the rescuer's skill and knowledge of water conditions. Heavy surf offers the principal obstacle to the use of a surfboard; consequently there are times when the torpedo buoy should be used instead of the surfboard.

The technique of launching a surfboard depends upon the weight of the board and strength of the rescuer. A method that is commonly used when the surfboard is near the water's edge is for the rescuer to pick up the surfboard about midway along the sides, run a short distance into the water, and without checking his momentum bend forward to drop the surfboard onto the water. Without releasing his hold the rescuer leaps onto the surfboard, contacting the deck with one foot as he lowers himself into position for paddling.

When the launching takes place in surf the rescuer should take advantage of any "break" in the breaker line indicating the presence of deeper water and a seaward current (rip current). He should also observe that the third wave in a series is usually the largest, and the launching of the surfboard should take place just after the breaking of the largest wave. When coming ashore the same course should be followed, unless the speed of the seaward current exceeds the speed that the rescuer can attain with the victim on the surfboard. In case the rescuer is forced to return to shore through the surf he should observe the following precautionary measures:

1. Keep the bow of the surfboard at right angles to the breaker line at all times to avoid turning over.

2. Avoid the shoreward side of a large wave, to prevent the stern of the surfboard from being lifted and tipped forward. When this position is unavoidable, sit up so as to shift the weight backward and thus prevent the stern from lifting.

3. Avoid the trough of a wave in the breaker zone to escape the weight and turbulence of a falling crest.

4. Try to "ride" near the crest of the seaward side of the wave.

5. Slide off the surfboard when the surf is heavy and guide the surfboard with the victim on it from a position on the side near the stern.

6. Anticipate a spill whenever possible and move toward the wave to avoid being struck by the surfboard.

Fig. 74a.   Approach

From a properly balanced prone position the rescuer propels the surfboard with a double overarm stroke toward the victim. He should fix his eyes on the victim or upon the spot where he was last seen. As the rescuer contacts the victim by grasping him by the nearer wrist he sits upright and drags his legs to check the forward progress of the surfboard. (See Fig. 74a)

When the victim is too weak to help himself onto the board, the rescuer pulls the victim's arms across the board and as he levels the victim by placing one leg under the victim's body he grasps the victim's nearer shoulder and pulls vigorously to draw the victim diagonally across the board. The rescuer then pushes the victim's arms and body for-

Fig. 74b.   Position for lift onto board

ward onto the center of the board and finally spreads the victim's legs until his feet are on either side of the board. The rescuer while in a sitting position then turns the board by executing a clockwise circle with one leg and a counter-clockwise circle with the other leg. (See Fig. 74b)

line is played out, lifts him onto the board, and both he and the victim are then hauled ashore by his assistants.

In rough water the rescuer may decide to slide off the board, readjust the victim on it and guide, stabilize, and propel the board from in the water during the return to shore.

Fig. 75a.   Position for turn-over

Fig. 74c.   Return

After turning the board toward shore, the rescuer assumes a prone paddling position, with his feet trailing in the water for maximum stability. The combined weight of the rescuer and victim should be distributed to keep the bow of the board above the surface. The rescuer should watch both the victim and water conditions during his steady but unhurried return to shore.

An alternative method is to ease out a surfboard having a line attached to a ring in the stern of the board. The rescuer paddles out to the victim while the

Another method of rescue is the "Turn-Over." In this method, the rescuer approaches the victim (Fig. 74a), grasps his nearer wrist, and without releasing the grasp slides off the opposite side of the board coincident with turning the board over in that direction. The board is now bottom-side-up with the rescuer and victim on opposite sides but with the victim's arm across the board. The rescuer then grasps the opposite side of the board, in preparation for turning it right-side-up. When dealing with a heavy victim, the rescuer should force down the nearer side of the board with his knee while pulling strongly against the opposite side.

After drawing the victim across the board, the rescuer moves the victim into a diagonal position, turns toward shore, and carefully slides into a sitting position on same. He then completes placing the victim in position (Fig. 74c) and assumes a prone paddling position for the return to shore. (See Fig. 75b)

Fig. 75b. After turn-over

LIFEBOAT

A lifeboat should be manned by a trained crew of at least two—an oarsman and a rescuer. In emergency situations, however, a dory skiff manned by just one rescuer can be successfully employed as a lifeboat. A single rescuer should not attempt to lift a heavy victim into a small boat when there is real danger of swamping or capsizing. While the rescuer rows ashore, such a victim can be supported by a line passed around his chest and under his arms and then tied to the boat. If he carries with him a piece of light line about twenty-five feet long tied to the boat, a single rescuer can leave the lifeboat to recover a submerged victim without any worry that the lifeboat will drift away.

The launching of a lifeboat in surf involves the same considerations of shore, surf, and current conditions as described for the surfboard. The lifeboat may be brought in bow first when the surf is light, but must be turned beyond the breaker zone and backed in when the surf is heavy. The expert rescuer with a torpedo buoy can contend successfully with surf that is too heavy for launching a light lifeboat.

Fig. 76. Ready to lift into boat

Lifeboat (Courtesy of G. C. Adams and E. Wessels):

This dory skiff is equipped with a "rescaid" (17) which adds to the efficiency and safety of the rescue procedure. Whenever possible the lifeboat should be manned with an oarsman and a rescuer. There are times, however, when the rescuer does not have the services of an oarsman and must carry out the rescue alone. During the approach the rescuer extends an oar to the victim, being careful to maintain a firm grasp on the oar while he draws the victim to the side of the boat. For better stability the rescuer should remain seated during this action, and at all times during the following procedure he should maintain a low position. The rescuer then instructs the cooperating victim to move to the stern where he is assisted into the boat over the "rescaid." If he is exhausted the victim will, of course, need more assistance, and the rescuer may experience difficulty getting him into the boat. If confronted with someone too heavy to lift into the boat, the rescuer should leave the victim in the water clinging to the stern, or if he is exhausted the victim should be supported under the arms while the oarsman rows everyone into shallow water.

A piece of light line about twenty-five feet in length with a shoulder loop tied in it attached to the bow should be in-cluded as lifesaving equipment if the rescue entails recovery of a submerged victim. This is particularly true when the rescuer is alone in a boat, as the boat is likely to drift away during the recovery.

An unconscious victim who has stopped breathing needs immediate re-suscitative treatment. The choice method, whenever possible, is mouth-to-mouth, and should be applied immediately (Figs. 88a, 88b).

10.

Lifts, Carries, and Let-Downs

THE rescuer should be skilled in the use of the pool lift and the one-, two-, and three-man carries and let-downs. These techniques enable the rescuer to assist the unconscious victim, also the victim who is too exhausted to help himself, and the co-operative exhausted victim.

POOL LIFT

The pool lift fills the need of the rescuer confronted with the necessity of lifting a victim out of a pool or onto a dock or pier. The rescuer should be careful to avoid injury to the victim by scraping him over the edge, or to himself by lifting with his back instead of his legs. When the rescuer cannot lift the victim out of the water he should support himself and the victim by clinging to the edge of the pool or dock while awaiting assistance.

The rescuer tows the victim to the edge of the pool in the cross-chest tow, grasps the gutter with his free hand, and moves the victim so that he faces the wall. Then, supporting the victim in this position by placing one knee under his hips, the rescuer places the victim's hands, one on top of the other, on the curbing.

The rescuer places one hand on top of the victim's hands to hold them in (See Fig. 77a) position and to keep the

Fig. 77a. Support position

victim's face out of water. He then moves to one side of him in preparation for climbing out of the water. (See Fig. 77b)

117

Fig. 77b.   Position for climb-out

Fig. 77c.   Lift

After the rescuer has climbed out of the water, he grasps the victim's left wrist with his own right hand and the victim's right wrist with his own left hand. He should stand as close to the edge of the pool as possible so as to permit a vertical lift and thus avoid scraping the victim's chest and abdomen on the edge. To avoid back strain the rescuer should lift by extending (straightening) his knees with his back as straight as possible. To partially overcome the inertia of a heavy victim, the rescuer should allow the victim to sink beneath the surface of the water before exerting a vigorous lifting action.

The rescuer may prefer to cross the victim's hands before lifting him out of the water. Such a cross-hand lift will turn the victim's back to the wall so that he can be lifted to a sitting position on the edge. The rescuer can then reach under the victim's arms to encircle his chest so as to drag him into position for follow-up treatment.

Fig. 77d. Moving into position

After the victim's body has been pulled over the edge, the rescuer should release the victim's wrists, step to his side, grasp his legs, and lift them into position for the follow-up treatment.

FIREMAN'S CARRY

The rescuer's choice of this carry should depend on the extent of his fatigue and on the weight of the victim. The rescuer should realize that he may injure both himself and the victim if he over-estimates his capacity to use this carry. The rescuer should use assistance when available during the let-down procedure. If confronted with the problem of carrying an unconscious victim up an embankment the rescuer can free both arms by balancing the victim across his shoulders or by passing a piece of line

around the victim's chest and tying it around the leg that hangs in front of the rescuer's shoulder. The rescuer should keep his head down and his upper back rounded to present a broader carrying surface. This procedure cannot be carried out, however, unless the victim is easily handled and the rescuer is prepared to extend himself.

Fig. 78a. Starting position

Carry:

The rescuer standing in chest-deep water supports the victim by placing one hand under the back of his neck and the other hand under his farther knee.

Fig. 78b.   Rolling onto shoulders

The rescuer assumes a stride position as he ducks beneath the surface and rolls the victim over across his shoulders to a face downward position, so that the crest of the victim's hip bone comes in contact with the back of the rescuer's neck. The rescuer then slips one arm between the victim's legs, encircles the nearer leg, and grasps the victim's corresponding wrist. The complete action should be executed quickly. (78b)

The rescuer stands erect quickly, so as to lift the victim's face out of the water. The balanced position of the victim across the rescuer's shoulders will permit the rescuer to use both hands for climbing. (78c)

Fig. 79a.   Leg support

Fig. 78c.   Completed carry

Let-Down:

The rescuer crouches, and grasping the victim's left wrist with his right hand, removes his left arm from between the victim's legs, and slides the victim off his shoulders to a straddle position on his left knee. To prevent the victim from sliding to the ground, the rescuer should apply considerable tension to the victim's left arm, at the same time forcing his head backward against the victim's armpit. Finally, the rescuer should slide his left arm under the victim's right shoulder and around his back.

Fig. 79c. Position on ground

in Fig. 79a can be used to pick up a victim from the ground.

SADDLE-BACK CARRY

The lower center of gravity and weight distribution of this carry enables the rescuer to lift a heavier victim and carry him ashore without undue strain. The rescuer is handicapped, however, when the bottom is rocky or slippery, or an embankment is at the water's edge, because he must use both his arms to hold the victim.

Fig. 79b. Slide to ground

As the rescuer releases his grasp on the victim's left wrist, he slides the victim's armpit over the back of his head, at the same time quickly encircles the victim's back with his right arm and grasps his left wrist. The rescuer then lowers the victim to a kneeling position.

As he lowers the victim to a prone position on the ground, the rescuer steps back. From this position at the victim's head, the rescuer then turns the victim's face to one side, opens his mouth, and pulls his tongue forward, while an assistant proceeds with artificial respiration, if necessary.

The reverse of the procedure shown

Fig. 80a. Starting position

Carry:

The rescuer stands in waist-deep water, supporting the victim with his right knee under the victim's hips and with his left hand under the victim's neck. From this position the rescuer reaches across the victim's body with his right hand to grasp the victim's left elbow.

Fig. 80b. Turn

After using his right hand to flip the victim's left arm around the back of his (the rescuer's) neck, the rescuer slides his right hand forward to support the victim's head above the surface. Coinci-

Fig. 80c. Carry

dent with the latter action the rescuer starts to turn his back toward the front of the victim's body.

The rescuer passes his left arm over the back of the victim's knees when his back comes in contact with the front of the victim's body. He carries the victim in a bent position with the weight over the lower part of the rescuer's back. While carrying the victim the rescuer should walk with trunk bent forward, so as to compensate for the additional weight and avoid straining his back.

Fig. 81a. Legs released

Let-Down:

The rescuer kneels on one knee, lowers the victim's legs to the ground, and turning to face the victim places the hand he used to hold the victim's legs under the back of the victim's neck. As the rescuer continues to turn, he lowers the victim to a prone (front) position, withdrawing his leg from beneath the rescuer's body, with particular attention to lowering the victim's head gently to the ground.

Fig. 81b.   Position on ground

After the let-down has been completed the rescuer places the victim's arms in a position of extreme flexion (beyond head) in preparation to rolling him over to the prone position.

ONE-MAN DRAG

When the rescuer is alone, the method of choice is the one-man drag method. A heavy victim can be brought ashore easier and quicker in this way and the let-down procedure is less likely to be traumatic to the victim. If the victim is a child, or light in weight, the rescuer, of course, may choose to carry such a person ashore in his arms.

The rescuer sets up the victim in knee-deep water, crouches behind him and, reaching under the victim's shoulders encircles his chest with both arms. The rescuer then locks his arms over the front of the victim's chest by grasping one wrist with the other hand.

Fig. 82a.   Drag

The rescuer should recognize that artificial respiration can be started at this time by alternately squeezing the chest. This procedure should continue until the victim is ashore where a more effective method should be employed. If the shore is unusually rocky or steep, the rescuer may have to remain seated to perform artificial respiration. Under these conditions the rescuer can improvise a two-phase method by squeezing the victim's chest (expiration) and then elevating the victim's arms (inspiration) at the rate of 12 respirations per minute.

The rescuer extends (straightens) his knees to lift the victim's hips off the

Fig. 82b.   Turn-over

Fig. 82c.   Let-down

bottom and walks backward to the shore, where, if assistance is not available, he will have to turn the victim over

to the prone position near the water's edge. The rescuer turns the victim over to the prone position by stepping across the victim's body as he lowers him to the ground. The rescuer is then in position to start artificial respiration immediately.

TWO-MAN CARRY

When assistance is available, the rescuer should direct an assistant to hold the victim's legs while he holds the victim's body in the manner used for the one-man drag. During the carry to shore, the assistant should avoid proceeding too fast so as to keep abreast of the rescuer.

The rescuer grasps the victim in the same manner as he does for the one-man drag (Fig. 82a) while his assistant lifts the victim's legs. The victim is carried ashore quickly, where his feet are lowered to the ground and the rescuer completes the let-down in the same way used for the one-man drag.

THREE-MAN AUSTRALIAN CARRY

This carry is used by the Surf Life Saving Association of Australia (5) and has real merit for use by a group of trained lifeguards. The victim is carried in a prone position with his legs higher than his head, so as to provide for good drainage of his air passages. Two rescuers support the trunk, one on each side, by passing one arm under the lower abdomen and the other arm under one of the victim's armpits with the palm of the hand in contact with his shoulder blade (scapula). The third rescuer places both the victim's feet over one of his shoulders and, to prevent the victim's knees from bending, places his hands under the victim's knees. In this way a heavy victim can be brought ashore quickly and easily and be deposited in proper position for resuscitation without danger of injury.

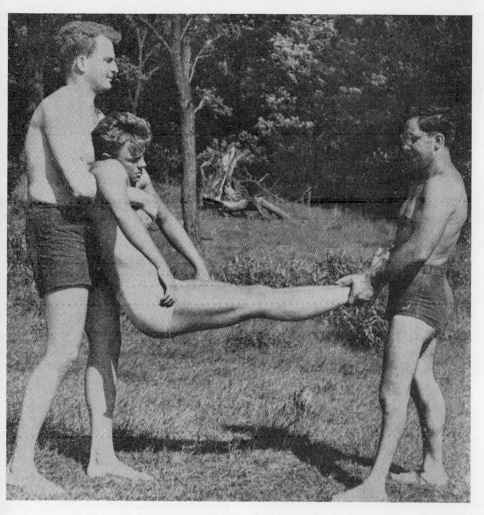

Fig. 83. Carry

STRADDLE-BACK CARRY (PICKABACK)

This carry is suitable when the exhausted victim is unable to walk and the distance he must be transported is considerable. Olson (91) states: "If he is unable of himself to get on his feet, raise him; then while supporting him, step in front of him, your back to him, stoop and have him pass his arms over your shoulders, and interlock his hands across your chest. Pass your arms beneath his thighs, straighten up, bringing

his body well up on your back. To hold him more firmly, after your arms have been passed under his thighs, grasp his left wrist with your right hand and his right wrist with your left hand; this will relieve him of all efforts to retain his hold. If he can use but one arm, grasp the wrist of the arm with your opposite hand. It may be possible to employ this carry for an unconscious person if, before you stoop, you draw his arms over your shoulders, and then quickly pass your arms beneath his thighs and grasp his wrists."

SUPPORTING CARRY

This carry is suitable for the tired victim who can walk ashore but needs some support. If the rescuer is on the right side he grasps the victim's right wrist with his own right hand, passes his left arm around the victim's waist, and slips his head under the victim's right arm. Then, maintaining a firm grasp on the victim's right wrist, he slowly assists the victim to shore.

11.

Resuscitation

THE NATURE OF DROWNING

To understand and apply the process of resuscitation it is necessary to know as exactly as possible just what drowning is. Flagg (49) presents the medical examiner's viewpoint (Dr. Charles Norris):

Drowning may be classified as follows: accidental, suicidal, homicidal, and deaths from natural causes in water.

It will be recalled that in ancient days in Europe, people were drowned as a punishment. This occurred in Scotland and England, and all over the continent. The last cases of official drowning that I have knowledge of were in Iceland in 1776, and in Austria in 1777. Usually women were chosen because it was considered that this was a less tragic way of disposing of the life of a person. And in some parts of Germany, to show how much they thought of their women, they were drowned in mud!

Death in water from natural causes is at times difficult to determine if the pathological lesions, namely, a fibrous myocarditis with coronary sclerosis or cerebral hemorrhage, is present; and if there are none of the classic signs of drowning and the chemical examination of the heart's blood shows that the sodium chloride content is normal, the determination is not easy. I admit that if death is due to a laryngeal inhibition similar to the sudden deaths due to the choking of the larynx with a piece of meat or other foreign obstacle, the determination is extremely difficult and may be impossible, unless the surrounding circumstances are ascertainable through witnesses. In all cases of drowning in which a history of diving is presented, a careful examination of the neck must always be made for a fracture of the cervical spinal column. Such casualties usually float on top of the water face downward after crushing the cord; naturally they die from drowning, and have the typical appearance of drowning. The death certificate, however, should include the real cause of the drowning which is, of course, a fracture of the neck with compression of the cervical spinal cord.

We can all realize the tremendous number of tragedies which drowning has brought upon civilization. *Drowning is an asphyxial death.* It is essential only that sufficient water be present to cover the nostrils and mouth. Cases of drowning in shallow pools with only a few inches of water have frequently occurred, the victims being children, epileptics, or persons comatose from alcohol.

Let me call attention to the classic description by Sidney Smith. He states that a person falling into the water sinks immediately. Deaths occur from shock, injury, or heart failure due to heart lesions or inhibitions. Usually the person rises to the surface because of the natural buoyancy of the body and tries to save himself. Violent attempts are made at reaching the surface; if the head is under water, the victim inhales a certain amount of water and thus increases the dyspnœa. When a person strikes cold water he swallows a certain amount of it and some of it reaches the laryngeal mucous membrane. This is really the first stage of drowning. It is known as "respiration de surprise." Inhibition of respiration ensues. This stage is of very considerable importance. In other words, a person may die in water, and if respiration does not start again he will not inhale water. Thus, although he dies from asphyxia, his body will not present the picture of a typical drowning case; in other words, water will not be present in the lungs, which will not be ballooned. Chemical examination of the blood of both sides of the heart will be negative. As is now well known, when a person drowns in salt water and inhales a considerable amount of it, the salt content of the blood of the left heart will be increased on account of the absorption through the air vesicles, for the reason that salt water contains more sodium chloride than does the blood.

There are also a number of instances in the literature of fairly well-authenticated cases in which perforated ear drums have caused syncope and consequent drowning. The post-mortem signs in the recently drowned are pronounced and they offer no difficulty in determination. The convulsive movements which occur in the terminal stage of asphyxia, in which automatic respiratory efforts cause water to be drawn into the bronchi and air into the air vesicles, produce the characteristic ballooning of the lungs. According to Smith—and the author believes that all authorities agree with him—the extent of ballooning of the lungs depends upon the duration of the terminal stage and the extent of postmortem signs, which will vary with the struggle.

As in almost all asphyxial deaths, the heart does not stop beating immediately, especially the right auricle, which may continue to beat after respiration has ceased. This is known as the "ultimum moriens Halleri." The beating of the heart is favorable to attempts at resuscitation; and if this is not delayed too long it will be successful.

According to Gonzales et al (54) :

Drowning is a form of suffocation in which the asphyxia is caused by submersion in water, or similar fluid. The same result can be obtained if the mouth and nose alone are covered by fluid, without the immersion of the entire body.

The cause of death in approximately ninety per cent of the cases of drowning is asphyxia resulting from the inhalation of water into the bronchi and pulmonary alveoli and the exclusion of air from the lungs. About one or two per cent of the deaths occurring during submersion are the result of circulatory collapse or syncope, attributable to the shock of the submersion, especially if the water is cold and the individual physically weak or sick. The remaining eight or nine per cent of drowning deaths probably result from a combination of asphyxia and syncope. However, it would be a matter of considerable difficulty to determine just what has happened during a submersion, and many statistics on the subject are based, necessarily, on judgments and not on facts.

Those individuals who die of asphyxia display a slightly different group of phenomena. In one type sudden chilling of the neck or chest, or inadvertent inhaling of water by a sudden gasp at the moment of submersion may cause a severe reflex spasm of the larynx and a rapid onset of asphyxia. The victim becomes unconscious early and then may inhale a small amount of water. This reflex spasm is quite likely to take place if the individual is submerged with his face upward, in which case water flows readily through the nares into the laryngeal opening.

Asphyxia, in the majority of cases, is the result of inhalation of water into the larynx, air passages, and lung alveoli. Under these conditions the individual, after submersion, struggles to get to the surface, becomes more panicky, and finally inhales a certain amount of water. He may reach the surface and gulp air mixed with water; severe coughing and expiratory efforts are produced by the irritation. This only increases the urgent need for oxygen and hastens the inhalation of water. The face becomes cyanosed and the respiratory movements become violent; water may be gulped into the stomach, the bladder and rectum are emptied, and unconsciousness sets in. After the respiratory movements stop the heart may continue to beat a little longer. The process of drowning usually takes about three to five minutes, but may be prolonged to ten minutes or more.

Observations of Swann et al. (131) on drowning are of interest:

Of the many European studies of drowning [reviewed by Cot, 1931] the French investigators in general agree that when submersion has not been so long as to vitiate observation, the victims are either white ("pale") or cyanosed ("blue") [Martin, 1932]. In the "white" victims death is ascribed to "syncope," with little or no water aspirated and little or no froth in the respiratory passages. In the cyanosed victims death is ascribed to obstructive aspyxia, much water being aspirated and much froth being found in the respiratory passages. Cot [1931] writes that ten to fifteen per cent of all victims of drowning are of the "white" type.

The blood oxygen declines toward zero within three minutes after the start of drowning, but the carbon dioxide, after a transitory rise, falls to the normal range. The pH declines to about 7.1. In fresh-water drowning, there is an abrupt and marked hemodilution, as indicated by rapid declines in the plasma protein, hemoglobin, chloride, etc. From 0.1 to 1.2 milliliters of water are estimated to dilute each milliliter of blood. In sea-water drowning, the converse—a strong hemo-concentration—occurs, with 0.3 milliliter of water to have been rapidly removed from each milliliter of blood.

In fresh water drowning ventricular fibrillation commonly occurs (four out of six dogs) after three to five minutes of submersion. Fibrillation was not observed in any of the five dogs drowned in sea water. During sea-water drowning, the heart fails about nine minutes after submersion. This suggests that the chances of successful resuscitation of dogs drowned in fresh water will, in future studies, be found to be far less than the chances of those drowned in sea water.

Although obstruction of the respiratory passages resulting from inhalation of water appears to be the major cause of death, Swann et al. (132) offer experimental evidence that there are changes in the blood caused by the inhaled water which must be considered as an important factor in death.

Phases and Prognosis of Asphyxia. Coryllos' (25) study of the phases of asphyxia is well accepted (49, 136, 137, 139). He states:

All students of asphyxia and resuscitation agree that the general term of "asphyxia" is a vague, confusing, and often misleading term. In fact, as it will be presently shown, asphyxia, whatever its origin may be, is composed of four distinct phases which follow one another, but they present different symptoms and different prognosis. Thus, for example, while resucitation is very easy at the first and second phase, it becomes difficult at the beginning of the third phase, very difficult at the middle of this phase, and quite impossible at its end, and in the fourth phase.

The whole phenomenon, from its beginning to the death of the animal, presented a remarkably constant duration of four to five minutes. This course was clearly divided into four distinct phases, each of one minute duration. These phases can be described as follows:

The first phase is characterized by apnea and rise of blood pressure. This apnea is due to the reflex closure of the glottis. I shall call it the phase of initial apnea. Rise of blood pressure at the beginning of asphyxia is a constant phenomenon in all forms of asphyxia. The duration of this phase is of about one minute.

The second phase is characterized by labored respiratory movements and continuation of the rise of blood pressure. The animal fights for breath; the non-anesthetized animal is perfectly conscious until the end of this phase and fights vigorously to liberate itself of the hood. At the end of this phase, which also lasts one minute, consciousness disappears and tonic and clonic convulsions appear. This phase can be called the "phase of dyspnea."

The third phase is characterized by arrest of respiration, drop of the blood pressure, and disappearance of reflexes and muscular tonus. The duration of this phase is also of one minute. The animal which presented clonic and tonic convulsions at the end of the second phase, gradually relaxes and becomes limp, its jaw drops, the sphincters relax and the corneal and glottis reflexes disappear. I shall designate this phase as the phase of "terminal apnea."

The fourth phase is characterized by rapidly progressing weakness of cardiac contraction and arrest of the heart. I shall indicate this phase as "arrest of the heart."

The prognosis is very different in each of these phases; in fact, when submersion is interrupted anywhere before the middle of the third phase immediate and spontaneous resuscitation always follows; on the contrary, in the third phase (phase of terminal apnea) resuscitation, which is still easy when submersion is interrupted at the beginning of this phase, becomes increasingly difficult as we approach the end of this phase. Although the hood was removed at the end of the third phase asphyxia progressed to the fourth phase and the heart stopped. Neither artificial respiration nor bronchoscopic intratracheal insufflation succeeded in resuscitating this animal.

This experimental evidence shows clearly, I believe, the importance of dividing asphyxia by submersion into four phases. Moreover, it shows the futility of artificial respiration and carbon dioxide in oxygen inhalation beyond the third phase, and the necessity of avoiding any loss of time by the immediate application of procedures which insure insufflation of oxygen into the lung. The fact that resuscitation is still easy at the beginning of the third phase while it is very difficult and often impossible at the end of the same phase and that the duration of this phase is of one minute only, shows clearly the paramount importance of time. Seconds count in asphyxia and often determine the life or death of the patient.

This experimental evidence illustrates the statement previously made that unless the phase of asphyxia is accurately indicated in the results obtained with different procedures of resuscitation, no reliance can be placed upon the results reported.

The extreme necessity of starting artificial respiration immediately is emphasized by the study of Lougheed et al., who found that "asphyxia may be maintained for only a comparatively short period of time if recovery is to take place. This time varied with the individual animal but rarely exceeded four minutes; in some animals recovery has occured after the trachea has been clamped for seven minutes, while other animals failed to recover after temporary asphyxia of two minutes' duration. Another interesting feature was observed in the time interval between the cessation of respiratory efforts during asphyxia and the cessation of expulsive cardiac beats. This interval varied only from eleven to seventeen seconds. If the asphyxia was maintained four or five seconds longer, resuscitation was of no avail."

Saklad (105) has called the interval between respiratory failure and cardiac (heart) failure the "resuscitative period" and points out that the duration of this period depends upon the "state of oxygenation of the tissues and blood and the condition of the cardiovascular (heart and blood) system when the respiratory accident occurs." The results of the resuscitative efforts cannot be expected to be good if the patient's cardiovascular system is poor prior to the asphyxial accident.

Effects of Asphyxia. In a paper on *anoxia* (oxygen deficiency) Chase (22) reports as follows:

Ganglionic nerve cells are more susceptible to oxygen deficit than any other cells of the body and the effects of anoxia on the brain are profound and destructive. Reflexes are abolished if anoxia exists for a few seconds and coma ensues if the cerebral circulation is interrupted from six to eight seconds. Brain cells are irreparably damaged if anoxia continues from eight to ten minutes. The centers of the brain survive for a longer period, from twenty to thirty minutes, and the spinal centers from forty to sixty minutes. Even moderate degrees of anoxia produce headaches, visual disturbances, irrational states, delirium and hyperpyrexia (high fever).

The myocardial co-ordinating mechanism

is extremely sensitive to oxygen lack and requires, under normal conditions, five times the amount of oxygen needed by skeletal muscle. During periods of great activity, the myocardium requires as much oxygen as the entire remainder of the body.

Krogh has pointed out that anoxia increases the permeability of the capillaries. This is an important consideration. There is a loss of blood volume with concentration of corpuscles in the capillaries and a reduced volume flow which reduces the delivery of oxygen to the tissues, and thus a vicious cycle is established. Krogh further states that the capillary stasis (stoppage) resulting from oxygen deficiency is irreversible after fifteen minutes.

BRIEF HISTORY OF RESUSCITATION

The most ancient of all methods of artificial respiration is mouth-to-mouth insufflation, which is recorded in the Bible (I Kings, 17:17-24 and II Kings 4:32-37). This method is now considered to be the best method. In 1938 Coryllos (25) wrote: "The mode of resuscitation that has given me the best results in cases of severe asphyxia is the immediate application of mouth-to-mouth insufflation. I know of no method of resuscitation more effective and more rapidly effective. In a number of instances with patients apparently dead, this method has produced striking results."

In a paper based on the early literature, Cary (21) states:

Among the various institutions that have been formed for the welfare of mankind, none appear more worthy of our attention than those that are calculated for preserving the human species. In the vast realm of human endeavor perhaps no body of men have been more instrumental in inaugurating a world-wide movement which had for its sole purpose the saving of human life than was the society at Amsterdam, instituted in the year 1767, for the recovery of the apparently drowned.

In the spring of that year a few wealthy and benevolent gentlemen of the city of Amsterdam, struck with the variety of instances in which persons falling into the water were lost for want of proper treatment when brought on shore, formed themselves into a Society for the Recovery of Drowned Persons.

The methods employed in the resuscitation of drowned persons previous to the establishment of this institution, and also those recommended by this society, were based almost wholly upon empiricism, and it was not until some years after the founding of the Royal Humane Society in London, in 1774, that any systematic study was made to disclose the rationale underlying the various methods which were then in use.

The members of the Amsterdam Society pursued their design with so much zeal and success that, in the space of four years, they had the satisfaction of finding that, in not less than 150 cases, drowned persons were recovered by the means pointed out and recommended by them in the United Provinces by advertisements and other publications. Their *first* object was to inform the common people, as well as the inferior practitioners of physic, in what manner to treat a person apparently lifeless; and their *second* was to animate them by proper rewards to pursue the methods recommended.

The general instructions published by this society are very interesting. They tell us that as soon as the drowned body was found, it was to be conveyed, extended upon a hand-barrow, a ladder, or some long board, to a barn, a shed, or other place under cover, where no house was near enough for its reception. Then it was to be laid out upon a table or bench, in a sloping position, the head higher than the feet; it was then to be stripped, laid in a blanket, and carefully examined to see whether any parts were injured.

The bodies of drowned persons, since they were generally found wet, cold, and stiff, were to be immediately well dried, placed in a temperate air, and rubbed with dry and warm flannels or a flesh-brush. If dry rubbing did not soon prove efficacious, then some spirits or coarse salt were to be sprinkled upon the parts and the rubbing resumed; the spirits thus used were the volatile spirit of sal ammoniac, or hartshorn, or eau-de-luce, mixed with brandy, rum, or malt spirits. The parts to be rubbed with steadiness were the back-bone, the sides of the body, the abdomen and breast, the palms of the hands and soles of the feet; other parts to be chafed with the above-named spirits were the temples, ears, and neck. These spirits were not to be applied in profusion.

Since the mouth and nose of drowned persons were often filled with mud and froth, this was to be cleared away with a goose feather, or by repeated injections of some lukewarm water, tea, or aromatic infusion—the body to be laid upon its side, that the liquid might run out.

If a small degree of heat was obtained from the rubbing alone, a recovery became very promising, and the body was then to be laid in a blanket (or in a bed where it could be had) between two healthy persons, undressed, who were to continue rubbing and gently agitating the body, to increase the heat to a natural state. But if the first degree of heat was not produced by the diligent rubbing, then dry heat was to be added, in bed if possible, by some bottles filled with hot water and wrapped up in flannel; heated tiles or bricks, so wrapped up, but used with precaution; also hot sand in bags, laid near the sides, the hands, and the feet but not to touch; and a number of cloths, alternately heated, were to be placed especially about the head, the neck, and the coldest parts of the body, and renewed as they cooled.

The introduction of air into the body was also warmly recommended. It was practised in two different ways and tended "to blow up the lungs, to renew the circulation or to swell the intestines to produce motion." The attempt to fill the lungs was made by the nose, and required a particularly constructed pipe, one end of which fitted the nostrils and the other of which received the nozzle of a small clean bellows that was to be worked cautiously and slowly, while the mouth was kept closed and the throat gently pressed back to make the air take its right course down the windpipe and not into that which leads to the stomach. The directions stated that when this operation was well performed it might prove of great benefit, but that it was difficult, and, without the pipe, was scarcely practicable. Further, if the bellows were not at hand, the trial was not to be made with the breath of the operator, which "has become noxious and unfit to enter any lungs again."

The other method was made by the fundament, in which case the bellows could be more easily applied. This latter method was much more frequently used, and it was strongly advised that when common air did not suffice to bring about some signs of life a more stimulating vapor was to be blown up the intestines, such as "the smoke of tobacco for strong bodies, or some aromatic herb, as sage, mint or rosemary, for the weaker sort." It was accomplished as mentioned above, by the use of bellows or the so-called fumigator—the operation being commonly spoken of as fumigation. When a fumigator was not at hand, it could be performed very satisfactorily by the use of the common smoking-pipe filled and lighted, the bowl of which was put into a common clyster-bag; or by two pipes inverted on each other and held together by a piece of strong paper, or joined by a kind of tinder-barrel. In the words of the translator: "While the air, vapor, or smoke is being introduced into the body, the belly must be gently moved and pressed upward with the hand; and the operation must be repeated and continued for a length of time until signs of life appear. When those are obtained, attention is then required, to go on slowly, and to give heat and motion by degrees but not to overpower, by hasty endeavors, a body then in so weak a condition as to be hurt by every inconsiderate attempt. It should at that time be kept in gentle agitation, by means of the blanket upon which it lies. The nostrils and throat are to be tickled with a crow feather; and powders or salts that provoke sneezing may then be used. The temples, ears, and neck are to be chafed with the volatile spirits mentioned above, mixed with brandy or common spirits; some raisin-wine, tincture of castor, or peppermint water, or other cordial, ought then to be put into the mouth, a teaspoonful at a time, and allowed to go down before another is given."

Keith, in his lectures on artificial respiration, remarks that mouth-to-mouth inflation, a form of artificial respiration, was also somewhat extensively used.

Regarding the advisability of venesection as an aid in resuscitation, I find that there was considerable difference of opinion as to its usefulness, but on the whole most authorities seriously questioned its efficacy; and especially was this true in England during the last two decades of the eighteenth century.

The society further recommended the use of *emetics* and *stimulants*, both internal and external, as accessory and useful means.

A survey of the case reports shows quite conclusively that various other methods of resuscitation than those I have mentioned had been used by the laity of both England and Europe from very early times. Most of them, however, were crude, dangerous, and inefficient. The so-called *barrel method* had been practised for many years, especially among the sailors. In this method the body was simply placed upon the barrel, face downwards, the legs of the patient being grasped by the physician or other assistant and raised to the horizontal, and the body then being rolled forward and backward. If we carefully inquire into the principles underlying this method we find that it has much in common with a method recently advised by Professor Schafer.

Suspension by the heels, or inversion of the body, and merely rolling the body on the ground were other methods occasionally employed.

Case 19:

"At Amsterdam, on the 29th of July, 1769, a boy of fourteen years of age, called Jacob Voorn, rowing with some others in a boat, fell overboard, and sank directly. More than twenty minutes elapsed before he could be got out of the water. He was then carried into a house, where, by the direction of Floris Loosjes, an apothecary, he was stripped of his clothes, laid in a blanket, and rubbed all over; tobacco-smoke was blown up into his intestines, and wind forced into his mouth, while his nose was held closed; and this was repeated. He was bled at the arm, and nine or ten ounces of blood were taken away, after which, upon the appearance of some signs of life, a little brandy was put into his mouth; the room in which he was thus treated, being thought too close, he was carried into a more airy room, where some more brandy being forcibly spouted into his throat, he roused at once, and screamed out. When he became quieter, some milk and water was given him to drink. He was then put to bed, had hot cloths applied to him, and was well covered up. He grew warm by degrees, excepting at the soles of his feet, and was delirious at times; but that ceasing, he complained of a pain and inflammation of his throat, which by the prescription of a physician, was got the better of in a few days, and the lad was totally restored."

You will recall that the Amsterdam Society was established in 1767. It was but six years later that we find an Englishman —a learned and judicious physician of London—had become interested in this Resuscitative Movement, so to speak, and it was in the year 1773 that this gentleman translated the memoirs of the Dutch Society. This booklet immediately arrested the attention of one of the most remarkable men of London, Dr. William Hawes, and the latter tells us that it was Dr. Cogan who first fired him with the purpose of introducing into London the methods practiced by this Amsterdam institution.

On the 18th of April, 1774, in the London Coffee House, these two men and a score or more of other friends founded the Royal Humane Society. It is of historical interest to recall that such names as David Garrick, Oliver Goldsmith, John Hunter, A. Fothergill, Frederick Bull, Lord Mayor of London, James Horsfall, Heberden, Lettsom, Beaumont, Parkinson, and many others appear in the transactions of this society as officers, members and supporters. Dr. Hawes and Dr. Cogan were the institutors of the society and the former was its leading spirit until his death in 1808.

The methods advocated by this English society were similar in many respects to those recommended by the Dutch institution. Their direction stated that the restoration of heat is absolutely essential to life, and, therefore, they emphasized particularly the application of warmth. Artificial respiration and especially fumigation were quite extensively used in the manner described above. Agitation was similarly recommended. "One or more persons should take hold of the legs and arms and vigorously shake the body, which procedure could be repeated by the assistants several times within the hour, if necessary." They further directed that if one hour had elapsed, "and there be no signs of animation, and any brewhouse or bakehouse be in the neighborhood, the body should be placed in warm grains, or ashes, little exceeding that of healthy persons. If so fortunate as to obtain a warm or vapor bath, it should be employed in conjunction with the other modes of resuscitation."

E. Goodwyn, experimenting, about 1782, was the first to discover that the tongue might fall back and thus occlude the opening into the larynx.

It is interesting to trace the fate of some of these various methods of resuscitation; for example, the use of the bellows. This method had long been in use by anatomists and physiologists on keeping animals alive during experiments, and it appears to have been first used in a human being by Dr. John Fothergill, of London, about 1750. It is also known to have been employed by the laity during the middle part of the eighteenth century. The bellows was first recommended by the Royal Humane Society in 1782 and for some thirty-five or forty years no word was registered against it. It was Leroy of France who, in 1829, showed that it was possible to kill an animal by suddenly inflating its lungs and also to produce emphysema of the lungs and pneumothorax in dead animals. He found that from twenty to eighty mm. Hg. pressure was sufficient. The fact which damned the use of the bellows was Leroy's statement that the lungs of those on whom inflation had been unsuccessfully performed

were frequently emphysematous. It was not until the publication of Paltauf's memoir in 1888 that emphysema was recognized as a consequence of drowning. As a result of Leroy's statement the use of the bellows fell into disgrace as a method of resuscitation.

Sir William Brodie was also instrumental in relegating the bellows to the past. In 1821 he stated dogmatically that there were few cases of drowning in which artificial respiration would prove of any service. His reason was that in from two to three minutes after respiration had ceased, the heart stopped, and when that occurred artificial respiration was powerless to restore it. It was of use only when it could be applied before the heart had stopped, and such cases generally recovered without assistance.

Because of these statements and Leroy's work, artificial respiration was regarded as an altogether secondary measure in the restoration of the drowned.

The history of the method of fumigation illustrates how quickly and how unreasonably a method at one time extensively used may fall into disrepute. It was undoubtedly used for many years before the foundation of the Royal Humane Society, and was employed successfully for some thirty-five years following the organization of this institution. Three experiments conducted in 1811, by Brodie, then only about twenty-eight years old, brought the practice to an abrupt close. He discovered that four ounces of a strong infusion of tobacco injected into the intestines was sufficient to kill a dog in from eight to ten minutes, and that one ounce could kill a cat. Nicotine was a cardiac poison. During the previous thirty-five years the methods had been found to succeed in hundreds of cases and had been warmly recommended by such authorities as Cullen, Cogan, Ward, Dixon, and Hawes. Three crude experiments by a young surgeon were sufficient to overturn thirty-five years of experience.

We now come to what may be designated as a new era in the resuscitative movement. I refer to the introduction of mechanical expansion and compression of the chest wall as a new method in recovering the apparently drowned. Dr. Marshall Hall was really the founder of this method, though artificial movements of the chest had been intentionally practiced before this time. It was Leroy of France, in 1829, who observed that the bellows, in the hands of an ignorant operator, might become a dangerous weapon, and proposed in its stead a method of artificial respiration quite like that introduced by Howard some forty years later. This method consisted in laying the patient face upwards and compressing the anterior wall of the abdomen and thorax, thus producing expiration, inspiration resulting from the elastic rebound of the chest wall.

The first systematic attempt to deal with this subject, however, was that of Dr. Marshall Hall, of England. In 1857 this learned physiologist published his paper entitled, "Prone and Postural Respiration in Drowning." The method is known as the Marshall Hall or the *ready* method, the latter proposed because no apparatus of any kind was required.

In analyzing this method, we find that the essence of it consists in altering the position of the patient from a lateral to a prone position, the supposition being that, with these changes in the position of the body, alterations would be produced in the capacity of the thorax, the front of which, in the prone position, would sustain the weight of the trunk and would thus be somewhat compressed, while in the lateral position the more movable front of the thorax would be relieved of pressure and would tend to resume its original volume by virtue of its elasticity. It should be added that the weight of the trunk is, in this method, assisted in the task of forcing air out from the thorax by pressure between the shoulder blades and over the lower chest when the body is in the prone position, and it may further be added that this pressure tends considerably toward the efficiency of the method.

In the following year, 1858, Dr. H. B. Silvester worked out a method of artificial respiration on quite a new principle. His aim was to imitate as nearly as possible the natural movements, and especially the raising of the ribs. He selected the supine posture. His experiments were conducted upon the dead body. With the object in mind of raising the ribs, he advocated the pulling of the arms forcibly above the head, thereby dragging upon the ribs by means of the pectoral and other muscles passing between the arms and the thorax, and so effecting an enlargement of that cavity by the elevation of the ribs. Expiration in this method is brought about by lowering the arms again to the sides and then compressing the thorax laterally.

In 1869, Dr. Benjamin Howard, of New York, published the description of another method, which depended, not upon traction or posture, but upon pressure alone. In his plain rules, Dr. Howard first instructs you to turn the patient face downward and press two or three times with all your weight upon the back, so as to press the water out of the lungs and stomach; then to turn the patient's face upward and (after producing overextension of the spine by placing a support under the patient, so as to make the subcostal margin prominent) kneel over the lower part of the body, placing a hand over each prominent subcostal margin so that the fingers occupy the furrows between the ribs above the margins, the palms below them. When pressure is applied by the operator placing his weight over his hands, expiration is produced by a triple movement; first, the lower six ribs are depressed; second, the abdominal contents, especially the liver and spleen, are compressed so as to force upward the diaphragm and empty the lungs; and third, the extension of the spine is partly undone. The pressure is relieved by a sudden jerk backward, and the spine again becomes overdistended, the lower ribs again become prominent, and the viscera slowly return to the position of rest. Inspiration is thus effected by the rebound. This operation is to be repeated from ten to twelve times per minute.

The most recent method which has been advocated for the resuscitation of the drowned was introduced in 1903 by Prof. E. A. Schafer, and his work undoubtedly is one of the most important contributions ever made to the literature of resuscitation. His technique was far more exact than that of previous investigators, and his experiments were made in a most thorough and scientific manner.

In 1932, Holger Nielsen of the Danish Red Cross presented his method and in the same year Dr. F. C. Eve was conducting his initial investigation. See Figs. 84a, 84b, 84c, 85a, 85b.

Eve (46), in 1932, rediscovered the old teeter-board method while attending a patient two years of age whose airway was nearly occluded with mucus and whose diaphragm was not functioning properly. He was able to cope with the problems by tying the child onto a rocking chair and rocking it back and forth. As the child's head was tilted downward, the mucus was drained off, expiration resulted, and when the child's feet were tilted downward, inspiration resulted.

Eve was one of the first to challenge the effectiveness of the Schafer method.

In 1933 (49) the Society for the Prevention of Asphyxial Death (S.P.A.D.) was organized for the purpose of making "the American physician 'asphyxia-conscious.'"

In 1935, Drinker and Shaw combined features of both the Schafer and Nielsen methods.

Also in 1935 Thompson (141) suggested the hip lift—prone pressure method but it remained unnoticed until there was a strong revival of interest in manual methods of artificial respiration.

Flagg (49) in 1944 wrote:

Professional asphyxia-consciousness initiated and developed by the Society for the Prevention of Asphyxial Death during the last decade, accepted and confirmed by the American Medical Association through the last five years, has prepared the ground for a serious approach to the problem of asphyxial death, especially for its institutional and group approach, and for the development of the art of resuscitation.

Without knowledge of Thompson's report, Emerson (57) proposed in 1948 the hip lifting method which has been combined with the prone pressure method and is now known as the prone (back) pressure—hip lift method or the Schafer-Emerson-Ivy method. See Figs. 86a, 86b, 86c.

About 1950 Gordon et al. (57) proposed the prone (back) pressure—hip roll method. See Figs. 87a, 87b.

On December 6, 1951 (72) the back pressure—arm lift (Nielsen) method was adopted by the American National Red Cross, Armed Forces, American Telephone and Telegraph Company, Bureau of Mines, Boy Scouts of America, Campfire Girls, Council on Physical Medicine and Rehabilitation of the American Medical Association, Civil Defense Administration, Girl Scouts of the United States of America, U.S. Public Health Service, and the Young Men's Christian Association.

In 1949 the first edition of the *YMCA Life Saving and Water Safety Manual* recommended the most ancient of all methods of artificial respiration, namely, the mouth-to-mouth method.

BASIC FUNDAMENTALS IN RESUSCITATION

Many laymen have become so concerned with procedures in technique, e.g., exact position of the victim's arms, position of the operator, how the operator should remove his hands, best location to place victim, how the operator should hold his hands, exact location of the hands of the operator, etc., that they have lost sight of such key fundamentals as the following:

1. Start artificial respiration immediately unless respiratory movements are clearly discernible. Precious seconds are wasted by the operator who attempts to determine if the victim has stopped breathing or if his heart has stopped beating. The method of choice is an expired air method such as mouth-to-mouth, mouth-to-nose, mouth-to-airway, or mouth-to-mask. Do not delay by debating the relative merits of expired air

methods with manual methods of artificial respiration. Send for a doctor, and notify the police and fire departments. Precious seconds are wasted by the operator who uses an involved method of turning the victim over, looks for the best location to place the victim, loosens the victim's wet clothing, or waits for the arrival of a resuscitator or inhalator. There is usually plenty of assistance available at the scene of a rescue that can be directed into productive channels by the operator.

2. If necessary, the operator should turn the victim's head to the side and use his fingers to clear the victim's mouth and throat of mucus, froth, vomitus, dentures, or other foreign material. Stretching the front of the victim's neck by extending (tilt backward) his head and lifting his jaw prevents his tongue from falling backward into his throat and obstructing his airway. An unobstructed airway is absolutely necessary for the passage of air or oxygen to and from the lungs. To induce reflex opening of the mouth of a semiconscious person, slide one's index finger "between (105) the teeth and cheek and then exert downward pressure." Use caution to avoid being bitten.

3. Without stopping artificial respiration, place the victim's head slightly lower than his feet for more effective drainage. Too steep an angle may cause abdominal viscera to press against the diaphragm and restrict the inspiratory phase. This is particularly true in heavy and obese victims. This position may only require moving the victim a few feet, which can be accomplished with the co-ordinated efforts of assistants. Be constantly alert to the possibility that the victim may vomit and obstruct his airway by aspirating vomitus. Try to anticipate vomiting by turning the victim onto his side and quickly clear away the vomitus.

4. Keep the victim warm, but not hot, by the external use of heat. Blankets placed over and under the victim, and the use of properly wrapped heated objects will maintain body temperature. Directions for the use of such objects are suggested by Olson (91):

A hot-water bottle should be about half filled. After the water has been poured in, expel the air from the unfilled portion by pressing it together, preferably without twisting it, and screw in the stopper before any air can enter. The absence of air makes the water stay warm longer. Test for a leak.

A hot-water bottle that is to be placed next to the body must be enclosed in a covering made of outing flannel, or wrapped in a towel firmly tied so that it will not come off. The stopper must not be left uncovered.

The best places for putting a hot-water bottle are at the sole of the foot, under the knee, between the thighs, on the abdomen, in the armpit, and under the small of the back. When a part rests on the bottle extra care must be taken to prevent a burn.

Articles improvised in emergencies must be covered with cloth or paper before they are applied to the body. Those for holding water must be filled full. Solid articles heated by fire must be tested, before they are covered, for the right warmth, by being held for a few minutes against one's cheek or elbow.

Eve (46) offers this suggestion:

"Remembering that the revival of chilled nerve cells is our goal, I suggest hot bottles saddle-bagged over the neck."

The rescuer should realize that his knowledge of techniques is enhanced by his knowledge of the underlying principles.

Duration of Resuscitation Efforts. Banting et al (6) are of the opinion that, "even though the heart beats are not heard by means of a stethoscope and the pulse cannot be detected, artificial respiration must be continued until rigor mortis sets in. In many of our experiments the cardiac complexes have been detected electrocardiographically for as long as twenty-five minutes after the heart sounds could not be heard with a stethoscope. Many such observations have been made in human cases. Among others, Birchard has taken electrocardiograms during the after death in a great many cases, and approximately normal electrocardiograms were obtained for upwards of one-half hour after all signs of somatic activity had ceased. Consequently—and this cannot be too strongly emphasized—the stethoscope is probably a poor instrument with which to determine whether or not a person is beyond the point of resuscitation. Prompt, adequate, and prolonged artificial respiration is the only treatment for drowned, asphyxiated, or electric-shocked persons."

According to Flagg (49), "muscles stiffen and shorten after death. For a short time after death, reaction of muscle sarcoplasm is slightly alkaline, and the muscle is then flexible. In from two to six hours sarcolactic and phosphoric acids give rise to rigor mortis: it begins in the face, then spreads to the jaw and upper extremities, then lower, and is complete in two hours. Rigor persists for from twelve to forty-eight hours. The onset is hastened by heat or cold; heat accelerates disappearance. Rigor disappears when muscle becomes alkaline again."

On the basis of this information it becomes evident that a definite length of time of two, three, or four hours should not be established inflexibly as the duration of resuscitative efforts in cases of submersion asphyxia.

After Treatment. Whenever a physician is present during and after a successful attempt to resuscitate the asphyxial patient, the rescuer should follow his directions and co-operate in every way possible. Occasionally a physician will

not be present, and the rescuer must act alone. In such cases the rescuer should bear in mind the following simple rules:

1. Continue to keep the patient warm.

2. Keep the patient quiet and on his side (105) with "hips elevated to encourage postural drainage," thus avoiding aspiration (to inhale or draw in) of vomitus. For maximum drainage, roll the patient over onto his abdomen. Use handkerchief or other suitable means to keep the mouth clear of vomitus.

3. Obstruction of the pharynx (throat) by the base of the tongue can be relieved by pulling the tongue forward with a handkerchief held between the fingers to prevent slippage or by elevating the lower jaw and extending the head.

4. Observe constantly when the patient is moved or transported for the possibility of vomiting or tongue obstructing the pharynx.

5. Additional treatment is in the province of the physician.

Which Method of Artificial Respiration Should Be Used?

The writer wishes to bring to the attention of the reader that the following paragraph was included in the first edition of this work and in view of the revival of interest and acceptance of the expired (exhaled) air methods it is increasingly more evident that we need to re-evaluate continually our reasoning processes in the search for the best methods.

Throughout the history of the development of manual methods of artificial respiration there have been "best" methods which have been staunchly defended by their advocates, blinded as they were by their lack of knowledge and objectivity. How long this method [back pressure—arm lift] will be considered to be the best method is impossible to say, but it is logical to believe that the future holds more knowledge and understanding, and in the meantime we should guard against the pitfall of illogical emotional justification of our procedures and continue in our search for truth.

Although the expired (exhaled) air methods are now the methods of choice, they are not the only methods and YMCA lifesavers will continue to be trained to adapt themselves to a variety of circumstances. This objective, however, can be achieved only by understanding the basic principles of artificial respiration as they are known today and the teaching of certain selected best methods. Karpovich (72) lends his support to this stand when he says: "It seems, therefore, of great practical importance that responsible lifesaving personnel should be taught more than one method, so that they can fit the technique to the situation. When every second counts, an early application of an inferior method may save a life, while the superior method will be applied to a dead person."

What, then, are the characteristics of the best methods? According to Karpovich (72), "The best method should, of course, be the most successful in restoring life to an apparently dead person."

1. It should provide adequate pulmonary ventilation. (72)

According to Safar (101), "recent research has shown that the only reliable methods of breathing for a nonbreathing victim are those which depend on inflation of the lungs with positive pressure through the victim's mouth and/or nose. These methods are called 'intermittent positive pressure breathing' (IPPB)."

Safar (101) offers an excellent case for expired (exhaled) air methods when he states: "The size of an average breath of an adult is 500 cc. (one pint of air).

Only 350 cc. of this breath get into the air spaces of the lungs, 150 cc. remain in the so-called 'dead space' of the air passageways, where no oxygen is taken up and no carbon dioxide is eliminated. Artificial respiration, therefore, must move more than 150 cc. with each breath into an adult to get any air into the lungs. Breaths between 150 and 500 cc. are borderline volumes and must be considered as inadequate for resuscitation.

"With mouth-to-mouth and other exhaled air methods untrained laymen moved breaths between 1,000 and 2,000 cc. in all victims. With the manual methods of artificial respiration, which rely upon compression of and pull on the victim's chest (Holger-Nielsen, Silvester, etc.), however, even expert rescuers could not move breaths larger than 150 cc. into the lungs of most non-breathing victims studied.

"The air which we inhale contains approximately 21% oxygen. One may question how air which has been 'used' by the lungs of one person can be good enough for artificial respiration. Although the air which the rescuer exhales after a normal breath contains slightly less oxygen and more carbon dioxide than the air which he inhales, there is still 16% oxygen remaining in the rescuer's exhaled air, enough to keep a non-breathing victim alive. In addition, during mouth-to-mouth breathing the rescuer breathes twice as deeply as he would normally, thus making his exhaled air (18% oxygen) almost as good as room air. As a result of his deeper breathing the rescuer is breathing adequately for two, namely for the victim and for himself, for an indefinite period of time.

"A non-breathing, asphyxiated victim can be reoxygenated with 5 to 10 deep inflations by the rescuer's exhaled air. In infants, only 'puffs' from the rescuer's upper air passages are used in mouth-to-mouth breathing. These puffs contain as much oxygen and as little carbon dioxide as outdoor or room air."

Experimental studies conducted by Nims et al. (88) and Gordon et al. (56) "have indicated the unequivocal superiority of 'push-pull' methods of manual artificial respiration in comparative tests on warm, non-rigid corpses, normal human volunteers with baribiturate-curare induced apnea (non-breathing), and hospital patients who have become apneic as a result of intracranial pathology.

"Spirometric measurements have revealed that the push-pull methods, which actively induce both inspiration and expiration, are more than two times as efficient, as regards pulmonary ventilation, as the Schafer prone pressure and the Howard chest pressure methods (push only). These push-pull manual methods include: (1) Arm lift—back pressure (Holger Nielsen) ; (2) hip lift —back pressure; (3) hip roll—back pressure; and (4) arm lift—chest pressure (Silvester)." (56)

The operator who uses a manual method of artificial respiration should remember to position the victim's head properly to assure an unobstructed airway.

2. It should assist blood circulation. (72)

Oxygenation of the victim (145) is excellent when expired air resuscitation is used.

"The circulatory (56) effects resulting from uninterrupted 15-minute performance periods with each of the various methods have been observed on normal healthy adult male volunteers rendered totally apneic with barbiturate-curare mixtures. With all of the push-pull methods the mean arterial oxyhemoglobin saturation was maintained at near normal levels; with the Schafer

method, however, the mean arterial oxyhemoglobin saturation reached an abnormally low level. In three of nine cases it was necessary to discontinue the Schafer method because of alarming cyanosis of the subjects."

Although a "push-pull" method (72) is more highly effective than the Schafer method in returning venous blood to the heart, the effect of artificial respiration on the blood circulation is, nevertheless, "too small to depend on if the heart has stopped."

3. It should not cause body injuries. (72)

Although this characteristic usually refers to the welfare of the victim, some concern has been expressed concerning the possibility of transmission of an infectious disease from the victim to the operator during the execution of an expired (exhaled) air method. Actually (101) there is little danger of infection because "the bacteria which are in the air passages and lungs usually do not produce disease in a healthy adult."

Rupture (102) of infants' and children's lungs may occur "if they are distended with too great a volume." This danger can be prevented, however, by the operator who controls the volume of inflation by "puffing" air rather than by blowing too hard. There is little danger of rupture of the lungs of adults by the use of expired (exhaled) air methods.

Distension of the stomach may occur if the operator fails to elevate the victim's jaw properly to assure a free airway or when excessive inflation pressure is used. Safar (102) feels that "it was always a harmless and preventable complication. When the epigastric (stomach) area protruded, most of the air could always be expelled by manual pressure over the stomach between breaths. During resucitation in the field this maneu ver may expel gastric contents too, in which case the rescuer must be ready to clean the pharynx at once."

A frantic operator using any method of manual artificial respiration can cause injuries to the skin and some internal organs by exerting excessive pressure on the patient's chest. Pressure control should always be considered by the operator, particularly if he is heavier than the patient. No method is dangerous when used by a properly trained operator.

4. *Provided that it meets the conditions of 1, 2, and 3, it should be the easiest to learn and to apply.* (72)

According to Dill (39), "Resuscitation with expired air breathing is simple and effective. It is especially useful in cases of injury to the body. It is readily adaptable to babies, children, and adults without adjunct equipment. Rescuers can maintain mouth-to-mouth breathing for an hour or more without fatigue even though the victim is twice the size of the rescuer. Skillful performance of expired air breathing is an easily learned, lifesaving procedure."

Safar (102) points out that "the teachability of mouth-to-mouth breathing is demonstrated by the fact that 90% of 164 untrained rescuers performed this method satisfactorily after one demonstration. Women and children who weigh 45.4 kg. (100 lb.) can ventilate adequately victims who weigh approximately 91 kg. (200 lb.). Safar (101) also feels that "no consideration need be given to timing or rhythm. Volume is more important than rate."

According to Karpovich and Hale (88), "From the standpoint of the ease of learning and operation, methods of artificial respiration studied may be arranged in order of increasing difficulty as follows: (1) prone pressure (Schafer)

(the ease of learning estimated by inference), (2) arm lift—back pressure (Nielsen), (3) arm lift—chest pressure (Silvester), (4) hip roll—prone pressure, and (5) hip lift and hip lift—prone pressure." Another study by Gordon et al. based on the observations and ratings of 667 Naval recruits and 124 Waves arrived at similar conclusions.

On October 1, 1951 (72), the Conference called by the National Research Council recommended that the first phase of the two-phase (push-pull) methods be expiratory rather than inspiratory. Therefore, the methods included in this text will follow this recommendation and will be called: (1) back (prone) pressure—arm lift (Nielsen) method, (2) back (prone) pressure—arm lift (Schafer-Nielsen-Drinker) method, (3) back pressure—hip roll method, and (4) back pressure—hip lift method.

It is recognized that the weight of the body in the prone position (72) causes some compression of the chest, which reduces the expiratory range to some extent. Although this is not true of the supine position, the disadvantage of reduced expiratory range is more than compensated for by the action of gravity on the tongue, thus preventing it from falling backward and obstructing the pharynx as well as for drainage of fluids and vomitus. Because we are dealing with submersion asphyxia, only methods performed in the prone position are included in this text. This selection, however, should not be construed to mean that these are the only methods, because there may be occasions when the patient cannot be placed in the prone position. The operator should be prepared to adapt himself to the situation, and whenever possible improvise a two-phase method by squeezing the victim's chest and lifting his arms. Karpovich (72) has an excellent chapter on "Manual Artificial Respiration Under Specific Conditions" in his book.

How Much Pressure Should Be Used?

Pressure variations of 20 pounds to 170 pounds have been reported in the literature (72, 76, 102). Although there is a relationship between greater pressure and greater expulsion of air from the lungs within certain limits, excessive pressure can cause body injuries (72). The American National Red Cross recommends a pressure of 30 pounds and the Danish Red Cross a pressure of 30 to 35 pounds, with lighter adjustments for children. There is, however, discrepancy between these recommended pressures and the pressures actually used in performing manual artificial respiration. Karpovich (72) conducted a study at Springfield College on 100 operators who weighed between 125 and 226 pounds. When the Danish directions for the Nielsen method were used the average pressure exerted on the patient's back was 67 pounds, compared to 70 pounds when the American directions were used. The range of pressure for the Danish method was 34 to 100 pounds, and for the American method 29 to 105 pounds.

It should be evident that the operator should make pressure adjustments in keeping with the size and age of the patient. This need is sharply brought to mind when it is realized that 90 pounds of pressure (72) may break the ribs of an elderly person.

A simple and effective method for operators to develop sensory perception in the fingers and palms of the hands, which is needed to control pressure, is to use bathroom scales mounted on a support about eight inches from the floor.

Back Pressure—Arm Lift (Nielsen) Method. While kneeling on one or both knees, facing the patient's head, the operator, or preferably an assistant, quickly places the palm of one of the

patient's hands over the back of the other hand and rests the patient's cheek on them (don't waste time, get started immediately, even though the patient's hands are not in the exact position) The operator then reaches forward with his extended arms to place the heels of his hands on the patient's back just below an imaginary line extending between the armpits. This position of the

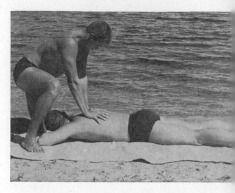

Fig. 84a. Starting position (Count 1)

hands assures a greater ventilation. With the tips of the thumbs just touching spread the fingers downward and outward to distribute the pressure over a greater area.

The operator lifts his hips to shift part of his weight forward onto his extended arms, exerting steady, slow, even pressure downward upon the hands to

Fig. 84b. Pressure applied (expiratory phase) (Count 2-3)

compress the patient's chest and force air out of the lungs. Although the operator rocks forward until his arms are nearly vertical, he can control the amount of pressure applied to the patient's back because his hips do not pass forward of his base of support. The duration of the expiratory effort is 2½ seconds which is timed by the operator who counts, "One-two-three."

On count "three" the operator releases the pressure and swings (rocks) back-

Fig. 84c. Lifting elbows (inspiratory phase)
(Count 4-5-6)

ward slowly, sliding his hands along the back of the patient's upper arms to a point just above his elbows. The operator then lifts the patient's arms upward and forward smoothly, keeping his arms extended, until resistance is felt. The arm lift expands the chest causing inspiration, by relieving the weight of the trunk on the chest, by pulling on the muscles that attach to the chest and to the arms, and by some extension (arching back) of the spine. The duration of the inspiratory effort is 2½ seconds which is timed by the operator who counts, "Four-five-six." On the count "six" the operator lowers the patient's arms to the ground and places his hands on the patient's back in preparation for the expiratory movement. The rate is 12 respirations per minute.

Nielsen recommends that his method

be modified for children under four years of age. His recommendations are: If it is a very young child—an infant or up to four years—the little body can be placed on a table or a bench if available, so that the rescuer can work standing up. Otherwise he kneels on both knees with the child between his legs, the head towards him.

Lay the child's arms down its sides and place a garment of some kind under the

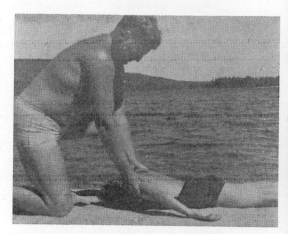

Fig. 85a. Pressure applied (expiratory phase)

Fig. 85b. Lifting shoulders (inspiratory phase)

forehead (or let someone hold its head up a little from the ground or table), so that nose and mouth are clear.

With the ends of the last three or four fingers on each hand take hold of the shoulders (between the ground and the shoulders), then raise the shoulders slightly and smoothly so that the chest will expand; then allow the shoulders to sink down, turn the hands slightly inward and, with the side of the thumbs, press very gently and evenly on the child's shoulder blades. Then repeat the slight raising, and so on.

These movements are made at the rate of fifteen a minute, i.e., two seconds for the pressure (expiration) and two seconds for the raising (inspiration). If the arms are injured, use the shoulder lifting inspiratory movement demonstrated in Fig. 85b.

Back Pressure—Hip Lift Method. According to Dill et al. "the hip lift—back pressure (back pressure—hip lift) method generally gives the highest pulmonary ventilation of any method studied. However, it soon fatigues the operator, particularly if he is small and the victim is large. It is the method of second choice (for military use); in case of arm injuries it would be the method to use."

Pulmonary ventilation (56) for the back pressure—hip lift method was reported to be 1140 cubic centimeters per respiration as compared to 1056 cubic centimeters per respiration for the back pressure—arm lift (Nielsen) method and 967 cubic centimeters per respira-

tion for the back pressure—hip roll method. The prone pressure (Schafer) method was 485 cubic centimeters per respiration.

While kneeling on one knee, straddling the patient at the level of his hips, the operator reaches forward with his extended arms to place his hands, with thumbs close to the spine and fingers spread downward, over the patient's mid-back at the lower angles (tips) of the scapulæ (don't waste time, get started immediately). The patient's arms may

Fig. 86b.   Back pressure (expiratory phase)

Fig. 86c.   Hip lift (inspiratory phase)

lie parallel to his head as shown in Fig 86a or his cheek may rest on the back of one hand.

The operator lifts his hips to shift part of his weight forward onto his ex-

Fig. 86a.   Starting position (expiratory phase)

tended arms, exerting steady, slow, even pressure downward upon the hands to compress the patient's chest and force air out of the lungs. Although the operator rocks forward until his arms are nearly vertical, he can control the amount of pressure applied to the patient's back because his hips do not pass forward of his base of support. The duration of the expiratory effort is 2½ seconds which is timed by the operator who counts, "One-two-three."

On count "three" the operator releases the pressure and swings (rocks) backward slowly, sliding his hands under the patient's hips (at the iliac spines of the bony pelvis, not at the waist) and lifts upward four to six inches by straightening (extending) his back and keeping his arms straight. The hip lift relieves the weight of the trunk on the chest and causes the abdominal viscera and diaphragm to sag downward, which results in active inspiration. The duration of the inspiratory effort is 2½ seconds which is timed by the operator who counts, "Four-five-six." On the count "six" the operator lowers the patient's hips to the ground and places his hands on the patient's back in preparation for the expiratory movement. The rate is 12 respirations per minute.

Back Pressure—Hip Roll Methods. This method provides effective artificial respiration in case of injury to the patient's arms or shoulder girdle, fatigue of the operator from the back pressure —hip lift method, or limited space in a boat. See Fig 76b. The starting position and expiratory maneuvers are identical to Figs. 86a and 86b. Just the inspiratory maneuvers are shown here.

On count "three" the operator releases the pressure and swings (rocks) backward slowly, sliding his hands under the patient's hips (at the iliac spines of the bony pelvis) and leans toward the side on which he is kneeling, keeping his

Fig. 87a. Hip roll—1st method
(inspiratory phase)

arms straight and rolling the patient against his thigh until the inside hip is lifted about two inches and the outside hip about six inches. The hip roll action causes active inspiration in much the same manner as does the hip lift action. The duration of the inspiratory action is 2½ seconds which is timed by the operator who counts, "Four-five-six." On count "six" the operator lowers the patient's hips to the ground and places his hands on the patient's back in preparation for the expiratory movement. The rate is 12 respirations per minute.

Changing Operators. Although time should not be wasted in changing operators, split second timing is not imperative. A simple procedure to follow for the Nielsen method is to have the wait-

Fig. 87b. Hip roll—2nd method
(inspiratory phase)

ing operator place his foot in position on the kneeling side of the first operator. Then, as soon as the first operator completes the back pressure action he rocks backward out of the way as the waiting operator kneels on the opposite knee and starts with the back pressure.

A simple procedure to follow for the back pressure—hip lift and hip roll methods is to have the waiting operator kneel on the opposite knee on the foot side of the first operator. Then as soon as the first operator completes the back pressure action he rocks backward and swings his foot out of the way as the waiting operator straddles the patient's hips and starts with the back pressure.

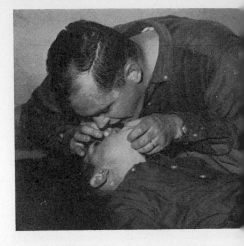

Fig. 88a.   Mouth-to-Mouth method

Expired (Exhaled) Air Methods

There are several distinct advantages of the expired (exhaled) air methods that Elam et al. present: "1. If the airway becomes obstructed, the rescuer senses resistance. 2. If secretions accumulate, he feels and hears gurgling. 3. He is able to see whether the chest expands during inflation. 4. He can feel the return of spontaneous breathing. 5. He has both hands available for airway toilet and for sustained support of the jaw."

The operator kneels opposite the left (or right) side of the victim's head, and if necessary he turns the victim's head to one side to clear the victim's mouth and throat with his fingers. To establish a patent (open) airway the operator extends (tilts backward) the victim's head with his right hand, inserts his left thumb behind the victim's teeth to grasp his jaw and lifts upward. The right forefinger and thumb are used to clamp off the nostrils. The operator takes a deep breath to assure adequate inflation and places his opened mouth at right angle over the victim's mouth so that the corner of his mouth is placed over his thumb to assure a leakproof seal.

The operator creates a leakproof seal and blows forcefully in adults, gently in children, and just puffs in babies. He watches the victim's chest rise until he feels resistance, then removes his mouth and releases the victim's nose to permit him to exhale passively. The operator repeats inflations every 2 to 5 seconds or 12 to 30 times per minute, faster for children and slower for adults. In case air is blown into the stomach it can be expelled by manual pressure on the stomach between breaths. To achieve

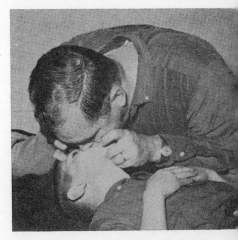

Fig. 88b.   Mouth-to-Mouth method

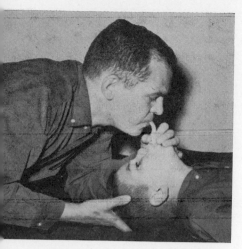

Fig. 89. Mouth-to-Airway method

reoxygenation of arterial blood the operator should increase the rate of the first few inflations without decreasing the volume of each inflation. It is important to remember that when performing this technique on a baby the operator will cover the baby's mouth and nose with his mouth. Another point to remember is that the operator can assist the victim's shallow natural breathing by blowing in when the victim inhales and removing his mouth to permit the victim to exhale.

The airway shown here is an S-shaped plastic instrument with a flange that fits over the victim's lips. There are correct sizes for children and adults. The operator kneels directly behind the victim's head, and if necessary he turns the victim's head to one side to clear the victim's mouth and throat with his fingers. To establish a patent (open) airway the operator extends (tilts backward) the victim's head with his right (or left) hand. With his other hand the operator inserts the airway over the tongue, being careful not to push the tongue back into the throat. The operator holds the airway with his left hand in such a manner that he can maintain a leakproof seal around the lips of the victim

and prevent his chin from sagging. The right hand may be used to pinch the victim's nostrils during inflation and to keep the head extended. The operator takes a deep breath to assure adequate inflation and blows into the mouthpiece, forcefully in adults and gently in children. He watches the victim's chest rise until he feels resistance, then removes his mouth and releases the victim's nose to permit him to exhale passively. The rate is the same as used for the mouth-to-mouth method.

The operator kneels directly behind the victim's head, and if necessary he turns the victim's head to one side to clear the victim's mouth and throat with his fingers. To establish a patent (open)

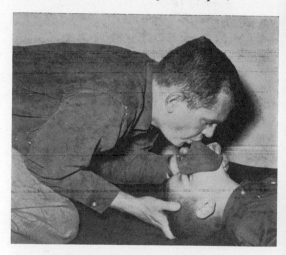

Fig. 90. Mouth-to-Mask method

airway, the operator extends (tilts backward) the victim's head with his right (or left) hand. With his other hand he places the rubber mask over the victim's nose or mouth in such a manner that he can maintain a leakproof seal and support the victim's chin. The operator takes a deep breath to assure adequate inflation and blows into the hole in the mask, forcefully for adults, gently for children. He watches the victim's chest rise until he feels resistance, then removes his mouth to permit the victim to exhale passively. The rate is the same as used in the mouth-to-mouth method.

Mouth-to-Nose Method

If the nasal airway is patent (open) and the victim's teeth are tightly clenched, which occurs infrequently in the field, or the victim has no teeth, the operator should not hesitate to use the mouth-to-nose method. The operator kneels opposite the left (or right) side of the victim's head, and if necessary he turns the victim's head to one side to clear the victim's mouth and throat with his fingers, which might be necessary in a case of no teeth. To establish a patent (open) airway the operator extends (tilts backward) the victim's head with his right (or left) hand. With his other hand he supports the victim's chin in addition to keeping the victim's mouth shut. He then takes a deep breath to assure adequate inflation, places his mouth over the victim's nose and blows, forcefully in adults, gently for children. He watches the victim's chest rise until he feels resistance, then removes his mouth to permit the victim to exhale passively. The rate is the same as used in the mouth-to-mouth method.

Gordon et al. (58) found that "mouth-to-nose breathing always worked effectively in these studies. However, in cases with nasal obstruction from edema, mucus, or submersion, mouth-to-nose breathing may be limited or impossible." Safar (102) found that "mouth-to-nose respiration failed in about 50% of the victims because of complete or partial occlusion of the nasal passages. Often the nasal passage was open at the beginning of the experiment but became obstructed by mucus later on. We tested the nasal patency of 100 healthy, conscious persons and found partial or complete obstruction of one or both nasal passages in 25%."

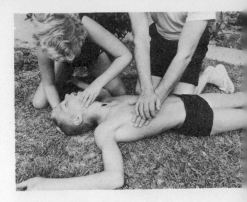

Fig. 91.
Closed-Chest (External) Cardiac Massage

Closed-Chest (External) Cardiac Massage (81). (See Fig. 91)

External heart massage can be combined with mouth-to-mouth or mouth-to-nose respiration when there is no discernible heart action or respiration. It is a simple but effective way, when used properly, to help restart a heart that has stopped for a short period. If the radial (wrist) or carotid (neck) pulse cannot be felt, then massage the heart as follows:

1. Place the victim on his back, and if an assistant is available, have him prepare the airway and start mouth-to-mouth breathing while the rescuer

2. Places the heel of one hand on the sternum (breast bone) just above the bottom end (xiphoid process) and the heel of the other hand on top of it and

3. Alternately pushes down after each lung inflation (12 times per minute) to squeeze the heart with controlled force, keeping in mind the age and size of the rescuer and victim (7, 23, 100) and release pressure to allow the heart to fill (100) at 1-second intervals or about 48 times per minute. Dura

tion (81) of the massage has varied from 1 minute to 65 minutes.

Even if the rescuer is alone he can try (100) "both respiratory and resuscitation by alternating a few lung inflations with sternal compression."

Fig. 92.   Compressing chest by squeezing

Modified Manual Artificial Respiration

The rescuer should be prepared to use artificial respiration when circumstances prevent the use of conventional methods. He may come ashore against a steep embankment, or he may drag the victim onto a rock, a narrow sand bar, a rocky irregular beach, or into a small boat, where he must adapt himself to the situation. Two-phase methods can be improvised by compressing the patient's chest (see Fig. 82a) and lifting his arms. However, expired air methods should be the methods of choice.

MECHANICAL DEVICES

The resuscitator should not be confused with the obsolete pulmotor or lungmotor, neither of which has been used for many years. Medical authorities found that these devices were dangerous to the asphyxial patient. However, even today an occasional newspaper account of resuscitation mentions the use of the "pulmotor" as a resuscitative device. This inaccuracy of reporting is unfortunate because of the tendency it has to perpetuate a term that

is now only of interest historically. Many asphyxial patients are alive today because medical acceptance has led the way to intelligent use by trained laymen of the alternating positive and negative pressure resuscitators. It is the opinion of the writer that all swimming pools and camps should own a resuscitator of acceptable design.

Safety. According to the J. H. Emerson Co., (104) "there is no known instance of lung damage from a negative pressure of 9 millimeter Hectograms (3 ounces per square inch) alternating with a positive pressure of 14 millimeter Hectograms (4 ounces per square inch) in the rhythmic cycle produced by modern resuscitators. (Over fifteen thousand are in use in the hands not only of doctors and nurses, but of police, firemen, and volunteer rescue workers as well.)" Schwerma and Ivy (109), in their study, state: "There is no evidence in this study that artificial respiration of the suck and blow type (14 mm. Hg. and 9 mm. Hg.) caused lung damage."

Coryllos (25) states that "it is also my contention that this apparatus can cause no harm in the hands of nonmedical but trained rescue squads."

Acceptance. A list of accepted resuscitators can be obtained by writing to the Secretary of the Council on Physical Medicine, American Medical Association, 535 North Dearborn Street, Chicago, Illinois.

Applications. Resuscitators can be used:

1. As resuscitators (alternate inflation and deflation of the lungs) when the patient is not breathing.

2. As inhalators as soon as the patient starts to breathe or if the patient is already breathing. When the patient is breathing or starts to breathe, the operator is warned immediately by the

increased rate of the audible tripping mechanism.

3. As aspirators when mucus, froth, or vomitus in the patient's throat obstructs the passage of oxygen into the airway. When an obstruction occurs, the rapid rate of the audible tripping mechanism is clearly indicated to the operator.

Comparison. According to Gordon et al. (57):

The properly employed mechanical resuscitator requires less skill than a properly executed "push and pull" manual method, is not fatiguing and can furnish 100 per cent oxygen; herein lie the most important advantages of a good mechanical resuscitator. There are other advantages, however. Since a resuscitator need be applied only once to a patient's face, it can be employed where physical manipulation of the body is impossible or would be harmful, as during major surgical procedures, in accident cases with extensive burns, broken vertebrae, ribs or arms, for victims trapped under debris of excavations or overturned vehicles and during transportation to a hospital.

From the foregoing statement it is clear that mechanical resuscitation, meaning the use of a resuscitator (rhythmic inflation and suction), is superior to manual artificial respiration. However, the resuscitator should not be considered as a substitute for manual artificial respiration until the resuscitator arrives at the scene of the accident and is actually functioning, and not a second before.

Birnbaum and Thompson (13) have demonstrated on dogs that the resuscitator is 95 per cent successful as compared to 55 per cent success when a single-phase method of artificial respiration was used.

Effect on the Respiratory and Circulatory Systems. According to Thompson and Rockey (138) "the two principal functions of resuscitation are oxygenation of the blood and the circulation of the oxygenated blood to the vital centers. Oxygenation of the blood takes place through pulmonary ventilation. Pulmonary ventilation has long 'been considered to be the sole requisite of resuscitation and, indeed, up to the time of circulatory cessation, adequate pulmonary ventilation may be all that is necessary for resuscitation to be successful. Once the circulation has stopped, however, the situation is drastically changed and pulmonary ventilation alone cannot be expected to bring about a successful resuscitation. The oxygenated blood in the lungs is of little or no value unless it can be transported to the vital centers and distributed over the body."

With these two significant considerations in mind, some knowledge of the physiological mechanisms of respiration should result in a keener appreciation and understanding of the complexities of the reflex controls.

From Guyton (62) we learn that, ... the respiratory center in the brain stem adjusts the rate of alveolar ventilation almost exactly to the demands of the body so that, as a result, the blood oxygen pressure and carbon dioxide pressure are hardly altered even during the course of very strenuous exercise or other types of respiratory stress.

Actually, there is no precise "center" in the central nervous system that controls all the respiratory functions. However, neurogenic mechanisms in the reticular substance of the medulla oblongata and pons can provide almost normal respiration even when the remainder of the central nervous system above the level of the pons has been destroyed. Therefore, this diffuse area is considered to be the respiratory center.

Located in the ventral portion of the reticular substance at the lower end of the fourth ventricle, are bilateral inspiratory centers, which, when stimulated, cause the muscles of inspiration to contract. Lateral and dorsal to the inspiratory centers are bilateral expiratory centers, which excite the muscles of expiration. The inspiratory and expiratory centers overlap each other so that movement of an electrode gradually from one to the other causes a gradual change from inspiration to expiration, or vice versa. In general, these two centers operate reciprocally with each other. That is, when one is stimulated, the other becomes inhibited.

In the lungs are many stretch receptors, located especially in the visceral pleura, that have a very profound effect on the rhythmicity of respiration. When the lungs become stretched, these receptors transmit impulses through the vagus nerves into the tractus solitarius of the brain stem and thence into the reticular substance. These impulses in turn inhibit inspiration. This effect is called the Hering-Breuer reflex. Inspiration excites stretch receptors that in turn inhibit inspiration. This prevents overdistention of the lungs, but at the same time it also has a very significant effect on respiratory rhythmicity.

The reflex operates in reverse during expiration: as the stretch receptors become unstretched the inhibition of the inspiratory center becomes reduced and inspiration begins anew.

In general, the factors that control alveolar ventilation can be divided into (1) chemical factors and (2) nervous factors. The three most important chemical factors are the arterial concentrations of (a) carbon dioxide, (b) hydrogen ions, and (c) oxygen.

Thompson and Birnbaum (136) are of the opinion that "suction, as well as inflation, in resuscitative procedures stimulate reflexly the medullary [respiratory] centers."

Experimental evidence concerning the effect of mechanical artificial respiration upon the circulation is presented by Thompson (140), who concludes: "We have described a method of observing the effect of mechanical artificial respiration upon the heart when the heart is no longer beating. This is done by the introduction of tracer substances into the vascular system of animals immediately after death and by observing the movement of these tracers while the lungs are inflated and deflated. The tracers used were radioactive sodium, fluorescin, and oxygen. By this method we have shown that the mechanical inflation and deflation of the lungs produces an actual movement of the blood column and that the blood can be circulated in this way over the entire body without the benefit of any heart action whatever. The clinical application of this knowledge in resuscitation is of twofold importance: 1. The oxygenated blood in the pulmonary capillaries would be transported to the brain and heart. 2. Intravascular medications would also be transported to the vital centers of the body. The value of heparin in resuscitation has been demonstrated. This (138) prevents clotting and keeps the blood in a fluid state. As a result the blood can be more effectively circulated, and this increases the possible survival time. Once the blood is clotted there is no possibility of any further circulatory movement. Those mechanical resuscitators employing alternating positive and negative pressures were far more effective in circulating the blood than were those machines employing only positive pressures alone."

Oxygen or Oxygen-Carbon Dioxide Mixture. Carter and Potthoff (20) state: "The Council on Physical Medicine recommends that the gas administered by resuscitator or inhalator to asphyxiated victims be oxygen rather than a mixture of oxygen and carbon dioxide."

RESUSCITATORS

Emerson Resuscitator. (Courtesy, J. H. Emerson Company)

While awaiting the arrival of the resuscitator, the rescuer should proceed immediately with the Nielson method to avoid losing precious seconds.

After the resuscitator is placed in position and is carefully checked to determine that it is functioning properly, the victim is rolled over onto his back and the face mask is placed tightly over his nose and mouth. The victim should be well covered with blankets to prevent further loss of body heat. Heating pads and hot-water bottles should be used to keep the victim warm. The operator

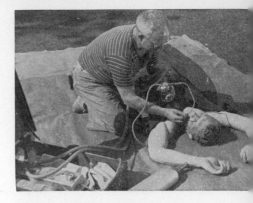

Fig. 93c. Using aspirator

and his assistants must bear in mind that the victim can be painfully burned by injudicious use of improvised or prepared means of keeping the victim warm.

Fig. 93a. Nielsen method

Fig. 93d. Dual application

When the presence of froth and mucus in the victim's throat interferes with the proper functioning of the resuscitator, the operator removes the face mask, introduces the aspirator tube into the victim's mouth, and sucks out his throat. This procedure is carried out as quickly as possible to avoid delay in the resuscitative process.

The operator slides the airway along the victim's tongue until the upper opening is even with his teeth, which causes the lower end to extend behind the

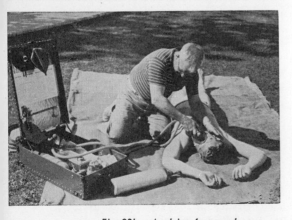

Fig. 93b. Applying face mask

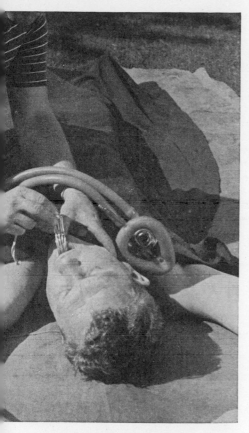

Fig. 93e. Introducing airway

of the most common indications for laryngoscopy are aspiration of semi-solid vomitus and laryngospasm. Laryngeal obstruction is signaled by the clicking action of the resuscitator, which means that air or oxygen cannot reach the lungs. This statement should not be construed to mean that laryngeal obstruction occurs in all cases of drowning, and, of course, the operator should not waste valuable time debating this question.

In the opinion of *Saklad* (105):

If the resuscitative effort is carried out where all desired equipment is available, an endotracheal tube should be passed.

Fig. 94. Endotracheal intubation

tongue and prevent the tongue from falling backward into the throat (oral pharynx). The aspirator tube can be introduced into the airway and suction applied to remove froth and mucus that may obstruct the opening into the larynx (laryngeal aperture). A rubber bulb syringe which should be kept in the resuscitator case will serve as an excellent emergency aspirator.

In the case of a double drowning a second face mask and aspirator can be quickly connected.

Although laymen are not yet trained in this procedure, the writer feels that members of special rescue squads should and will be trained to intubate the asphyxial patient when indicated. Two

They can be obtained in all sizes. Such a tube can be passed either through the mouth or the nose. It is best to pass the oral endotracheal tube under direct vision. For this it is necessary that one have at hand a laryngoscope, endotracheal tubes, and suction equipment. If one is experienced, it is not difficult to pass an endotracheal tube by the nasal route blindly. The mask of the resuscitating apparatus can be placed on the face over such a tube. Compressed air or oxygen can thus be delivered directly to the respiratory tract.

Appendix

YMCA LIFESAVING STUDENT PERSONAL INFORMATION

Name ....

Address ....

      (City)   (State)   (Zip Code)

Age .... *Date of Birth* ....

                                          (Month)   (Day)   (Year)

Name of my YMCA ....

Date course began ....

Date course finished ....

Results of final examination:
    Practical work (check) passed .... *failed* ....

    Written examination grade ....

CERTIFIED YMCA LIFESAVER

YOUNG MEN'S **CHRISTIAN ASSOCIATION**

The above named candidate has successfully completed the
NATIONAL YMCA LIFESAVING INSTRUCTIONAL PROGRAM AND TESTS
and is entitled to official recognition as

JUNIOR LIFESAVER................ SENIOR LIFESAVER................

Signed ....
                    (Name of official who certified above named candidate)

Position ....
                        (or title of certifying official)

Association .... *Date* ....

[See elsewhere complete list of lifesaving and water safety requirements]

Are You a Good Swimmer?*

To MAKE PROGRESS and succeed in lifesaving you must have good all-around swimming ability. This means you have mastered the progressive skills of the YMCA "Minnow" (beginner), "Fish" (low intermediate), "Flying Fish" (middle intermediate), and "Shark" (high intermediate). Through these tests or their equivalents you have prepared yourself to pass these pre-lifesaving tests:

1. Tread water at least 60 seconds.

2. Stay afloat on your back and front for a total of 5 minutes.

3. Do surface diving: feet-first and head-first surface dives, and swim at least 20 feet under water.

4. Swim at least a quarter of a mile demonstrating the following strokes: crawl, breast stroke, side and lifesaving towing strokes on either side.

When you can pass these suggested tests you are ready to start lifesaving.
Saving lives depends upon your *skill, endurance,* and *attitude.*

Skill means saving yourself, assisting others without swimming, as well as making swimming rescues and giving resuscitation.

Endurance means bodily strength, strong heart and lungs, ability to keep going indefinitely, to survive in the face of great difficulty and even hardships, and at the same time help others. Remember endurance is built gradually, during the training program, through hard work.

Attitude means respect for the water and the dangers that may be present, and also confidence developed through training, as well as ability to meet emergency situations in the safest manner possible.

---

* By Harold T. Friermood, Senior Director Health and Physical Education, National Board of YMCAs.

This is What You Do to Become a YMCA Lifesaver*

1. Receive instructor's recommendation that you are a dependable person worthy of becoming a YMCA Lifesaver.

2. Meet age requirements:
      Juniors: At least 12 years old and under 15
      Seniors: 15 years and over

3. Master the fundamental skills of the progressively graded YMCA swimming and pre-lifesaving program or the equivalent.

4. Submit evidence (a medical report and/or take a physical fitness test) to indicate you are physically able to carry on the activity involved in lifesaving.

5. Complete satisfactorily all items listed in the practical water ability tests for YMCA lifesaving.

6. Pay fees required for registration and purchase of the handbook *Lifesaving and Water Safety Today.*

7. Participate in twenty-two hours of instruction and conditioning, which includes the time for actual testing.

8. Score a minimum grade on the written examination of 60 for Juniors or 75 for Seniors.

9. Upon satisfactory completion of tests and other requirements purchase and wear YMCA emblem.

10. Review and repeat the practical and theoretical examination every year. (The annual recertification tests and procedures can be accomplished within a period of two hours.)

---

* By Harold T. Friermood.

Student Responsibility to the Instructor*

A COURSE in lifesaving requires careful preparation and planning by your instructor. You can assist him and receive the greatest benefit yourself if you:

1. Attend every class session.

2. Arrive promptly ready for action.

3. Keep in good physical condition.

4. Extend your knowledge of lifesaving—read newspaper and magazine accounts and discuss them with other pupils and the instructor.

5. Review other books in the YMCA Aquatic literature. As you gain experience you will want to study the various units in the *New YMCA Aquatic Workbook.* It gives valuable and complete information about the total YMCA aquatic program.

6. Work hard and prepare yourself for service.

(See elsewhere for complete list of YMCA lifesaving and water-safety requirements.)

---

* By Harold T. Friermood.

Instructor Responsibility to the Student*

EACH STUDENT enrolling in a lifesaving course has certain hopes and expectations that the instructor should know. This may require some personal checking with individuals or with the class as a whole, to discover these needs. Also, the instructor should state clearly what the course will and will not cover. The instructor should:

1. Prepare carefully for each class session.
2. Arrive ahead of schedule to make sure that facilities, equipment, and spaces are ready for use.
3. Keep in good physical condition; the instructor sets an example for others.
4. Keep studying to make sure the latest and best information on lifesaving is understood and made available.
5. Make sure that students understand thoroughly material presented. Ask questions, have ideas explained by class members, work in pairs, have one student tell the other what has been said, and have the other student make corrections. Do the same in practical work.
6. In giving the written and practical water-work examinations, make sure that every student "knows his stuff," and is thoroughly capable when certified by you. This is for his own protection, and to safeguard others. The YMCA Lifesaver is a person who: *knows* and *can do*.

---

* By Harold T. Friermood.

Practical Water-Work Screening Test*

IN ORDER to demonstrate ability and fitness as a rescuer, in making a complete rescue, and giving resuscitation to the victim, no stops or rests should be made during the following tests:

Test Items	Senior	Junior
Jog	100 yards	50 yards
Approach swim	100 yards	50 yards
Underwater approach and recovery of victim from bottom	8 ft. depth	6 ft. depth
Tow	80 yards	40 yards
Tired swimmer's support	5 minutes	3 minutes
Release (front head-hold and body scissors)		Same
Defensive tactics (rear-pivot breakaway)		Same
Control tow	20 feet	10 feet
Pool lift		Same
Demonstrate artificial respiration	5 minutes	Same

* By Harold T. Friermood.

Hints on Personal Physical Fitness*

PHYSICAL FITNESS is a very large part of the needed ability to lift subjects, hold the breath, outlast an opponent, carry a subject a long way, or sustain oneself at the surface of the water for an hour or more. In a death-grip situation the survivor may be the one who can last the longest in the struggle or hold his breath the longest underwater. Every lifesaver should practice the test items (shown on the opposite page) time and again for the purpose of achieving a superior rating by the time the lifesaving course is over.

Passing the test with a rating of "Good" or better is proposed, and lifesavers should not be recommended for public guards who are not up to this standard. It is deplorable to have public life guards who are not fit to meet an emergency and who show little respect for the fitness objective by smoking, drinking or overeating. Every employed life guard should swim a quarter of a mile a day and run a half a mile. Even more strenuous combative and underwater practice should be engaged in at least once each week.

Physical fitness may be gained by taking the physical fitness 10-item test each day that endurance running, swimming, and combative water-work cannot be done. The test aims to develop a stronger heart, better breath-holding ability, greater muscular endurance in the arms and legs for crawl, side, and breast stroke movements. A passing grade of at least "Good" should be required of Leader-Examiners who are engaged for paid aquatic service.

---

* By Thomas K. Cureton, Jr., Honorary Chairman of the National YMCA Aquatic Committee.

PHYSICAL FITNESS TEST FOR AQUATIC LEADERSHIP*

Items	Specifications	Poor 25	Average 50	Good 75	Superior 100	Points Earned
1. Five-minute Step-Test and Pulse Count on 17" Chair	Sum the pulse count at 1:00 to 1:30; 2:00 to 2:30; 3:00 to 3:30	190+	160	130	110	....
2. Trunk Flexion Forward with Legs Held Down, Feet 18" Apart	Three preliminary bends, then test slowly, forehead to floor	12"	9"	7"	5"	....
3. Trunk Extension Backward with Hips Held Down	Three preliminary lifts, then test slowly, chin to floor, then up	8"	14"	18"	20"	....
4. Extension Press-up from Hands and Toes with Body Straight	Keep elbows straight, lift body up off floor	0	1	5	10	....
5. Side Leg-Raisings (Right Hand Down)	Legs and body straight, raise leg to horizontal	15	25	35	50	....
6. Side Leg-Raisings (Left Hand Down)	Legs and body straight, raise leg to horizontal	15	25	35	50	....
7. Flutter-Kicks on Back, Knees Straight	Close to floor, ankles 8" apart in kick	50	100	200	300	....
8. Flutter-Kicks on Front, Head and Chest Arched	With straight legs, 8" apart in kick	200	400	600	800	....
9. Run in Place Co-ordinated Crawl for 2' Plus Breath Holding	After run, take three deep breaths and hold the third for time	10 sec.	30	45	60	....
10. Breast Stroke, Full Squat Jump	Touch floor with hands each time	25	50	75	100	....

Rating Scale:
Very Superior 900-1000 Points
Superior 800- 899 Points
Good 700- 799 Points
Fair 600- 699 Points
Poor 500- 599 Points

Sum of Total Points Earned ....

* As arranged and used by Thomas K. Cureton in numerous YMCA Physical Fitness and Aquatic Institutes.

YMCA Aquatic Program Information*

There are four levels of aquatic ability in the general YMCA program. These are:

Minnow club (beginner) .... 21 skills

Fish club (low intermediate) .... 10 skills

Flying Fish club (middle intermediate) .... 10 skills

Shark club (high intermediate) .... 10 skills

Total—51 skills

Note that the 28 lifesaving items shown on the Student Progress Record run from 52-79 in the consecutive skills numbering and constitute a fifth level of aquatic accomplishment. The addition of requirements for skin and scuba divers and leadership certification (Scuba Leader-Examiner and Scuba Instructor), authorized during the Fourth National YMCA Aquatic Conference, gave added scope and interest to the program. The program was further enhanced during the Fifth National YMCA Aquatic Conference by approving the 10-item Porpoise Club Advanced Watermanship Skills and the three grade levels of diving-skill proficiency represented by YMCA "Diver," "Advanced Diver," and "Varsity Diver."

* By Harold T. Friermood.

Student Progress Record

NATIONAL YMCA LIFESAVING*

Test Items—28 Skills

JUNIOR—under 15 yrs.
SENIOR—15 yrs. and over.

(Name)

	Date Passed
PERSONAL SAFETY	
(52) 1—Disrobe and rescue self	....
(53) 2—Deal with cramp ..	....
NONSWIMMING ASSISTS	
(54) 3—Reaching assists ...	....
(55) 4—Wading assists	....
SWIMMING ASSISTS	
(56) 5—Tired swimmer support	....
(57) 6—Tired swimmer assist	....
(58) 7—Assist novice	....
APPROACHES AND TOWS	
(59) 8—Entries	....
(60) 9—Surface approaches, (rear and front) ...	....
(61) 10—Underwater approaches and recovery of submerged victim	....
(62) 11—Tows (cross-chest, control, hair, head, armpit, leg support, multiple)	....
DEFENSIVE TACTICS, RELEASES AND WATER-WRESTLING	
(63) 12—Two-hand block and foot block	....
(64) 13—Rear pivot breakaway	....
(65) 14—Front parry	....

	Date Passed
(66) 15—Double grip on one arm, release	....
(67) 16—Front head hold releases (front head hold and body scissors, and front head hold release)	....
(68) 17—Rear head hold releases (regular, and somersault release) ...	....
(69) 18—Would-be rescuer release	....
(70) 19—Water wrestling ...	....
EQUIPMENT RESCUES	
(71) 20—Shoulder loop and line	....
(72) 21—Buoy rescue	....
(73) 22—Heaving lines	....
(74) 23—Surfboard	....
(75) 24—Lifeboat	....
LIFTS, CARRIES AND LET-DOWNS	
(76) 25—Pool lift	....
(77) 26—One-man carries: fireman, saddle-back, one-man drag, pick-a-back carry, supporting carry	....
(78) 27—Two- and three-man carries	....
RESUSCITATION	
(79) 28—Complete rescue and resuscitation, demonstrating three methods of resuscitation	....

---

* By Harold T. Friermood.

YMCA Certified Aquatic Leader-Examiner (Men and Women)*

THIS CATEGORY is for lay leaders who have unusual watermanship ability and desire to gain teaching experience by assisting the professional leaders. The Leader-Examiner may assist as a tutor or counselor with any phase of the aquatic program. In all cases, however, the Leader-Examiner renders service under the supervision of a professional aquatic director or instructor. The specific requirements follow:

1. Minimum age of seventeen.

2. Satisfactory completion of all the YMCA progressive swimming skills including 1) The Beginner's Full Length Test (minnow club); 2) The Low Intermediate Progressive Test (fish club); 3) The Middle Intermediate Progressive Test (flying fish club); 4) The High Intermediate and Pre-Lifesaving Test (shark club); 5) The Lifesaving and Water Safety Test.

3. Is familiar with the YMCA Porpoise Club and Springboard Diving programs.

4. Serve as an assistant to the aquatic director or instructor for a minimum of twenty-five class periods with such efficiency as to gain his or her recommendation.

5. Demonstrate satisfactory knowledge of the principles and theory of the National YMCA Aquatic Program as based upon the literature describing the National YMCA Aquatic Program and procedures by completing the informational examination with a passing grade.

6. Attend and participate in at least one YMCA Aquatic Institute or Leadership Training School before certification; renew credentials every two years by application and attendance at an aquatic school or institute, completion of practical water-work, theoretical work, and written examination.

At the time of enrollment for the course of instruction, the applicant should pay a registration fee to cover the cost of supplies, literature, application blanks, testing forms, overhead and incidental costs, etc., to the aquatic director, instructor, or local Association providing the application and examination forms.

The YMCA certified Aquatic Leader-Examiner's emblem and recognition card may be secured through the Field Agent or Aquatic Commissioner upon payment of the proper fee, if this has not been included in the institute fee.

---

* By Harold T. Friermood.

```
┌─────────────────────────┐
│                         │
│      Paste your         │
│      Photograph         │
│        here             │
│                         │
│                         │
└─────────────────────────┘
```

YMCA LIFESAVING INSTRUCTOR PERSONAL INFORMATION*

Name ....

Address ....
        (No.)   (Street)

        (City)   (State)   (Zip Code)

Age .... *Date of Birth* ....
                                            (Month) (Day) (Year)

Name of my YMCA ....

My level of YMCA Aquatic Leadership Certification:

Leader-Examiner	Instructor	Director
(Date certified)	(Date)	(Date)
(Place Certified)	(Place)	(Place)
(Certified by)	(By)	(By)

LOG OF YMCA LIFESAVING COURSES CONDUCTED

| | Number Enrolled | | Number Certified | | |
Date	Junior	Senior	Junior	Senior	Remarks
1.					
2.					
3.					
4.					
5.					
6.					
7.					
8.					
9.					
10.					

* By Harold T. Friermood.

Bibliography

1. *Accident Facts.* Chicago: National Safety Council, Incorporated, 1963.

2. American Red Cross, *Life Saving and Water Safety*, Philadelphia: P. Blakiston's Son & Co., 1937.

3. Andrews, W. D., *Swimming and Life Saving.* Toronto: William Briggs, 1889.

4. "Artificial Respiration: The Holger Nielsen Method," *Lancet*, 229: 437, (July, 1935).

5. *The Australian Surf Life Saving Handbook.* (20th Edition) First Edition, 1907, Sydney: The Surf Life Saving Association of Australia, 1957.

6. Banting, F. G., Hall, G. E., Janes, J. M., Leibel, B. and Lougheed, D. W., "Physiological Studies in Experimental Drowning," *Canadian M.A.J.*, (Sept., 1938).

7. Baringer, J. R., et al., "External Cardiac Massage," *The New England Journal of Medicine*, 265: 62-65, (July 13, 1961).

8. Barnett, Donald, "Water Safety, Life Saving and Swimming in the Mid-West," *Beach and Pool*, 11: 12, (Oct., 1937).

9. Bates, G., Gaby, R. E. and MacLachlan, W., "The Need for Prolonged Artificial Respiration in Drowning Asphyxiation and Electric Shock," *Canadian M.A.J.*, 39: 120, (1938).

10. Beck, C. S., *Resuscitation and Artificial Hypothermia.* New York: Consultants Bureau Enterprises Inc., 1962.

11. Berge, V. and Lanier, H. W., *Pearl Diver.* New York: The Sun Dial Press, Inc., 1937.

12. Best, C. H. and Taylor, N. B., *The Physiological Basis of Medical Practice.* Baltimore: Williams and Wilkins Co., 1955.

13. Birnbaum, G. L. and Thompson, S. A., "Pulmonary and Blood Gas Studies in Experimental Asphyxia and Asphyxial (Anoxia) Resuscitation," *Jr. of Thoracic Surgery*, 12: 607-623, (Oct., 1943).

14. Birnbaum, G. L. and Thompson, S. A., "Resuscitation in Advanced Asphyxia," *J.A.M.A.*, 118: 1364-1367, (April 18, 1942).

15. Bishop, M. W., "A Yardstick for Aquatic Freedom," *Safety Education*, 14: 219-221, (June, 1935).

16. Boushey, E. E. and Heyman, H. S., "Experimental Life Saving," *Journal of Health and Physical Education*, 5: 26-29, (April, 1934).

17. Boy Scouts of America, *Swimming, Water Sports, and Safety.* New York: Boy Scouts of America, 1938.

18. Boy Scouts of America, *Life Saving.* New York: Merit Badge Series, 1944.

19. Bretz, J. Harlen, *Earth Sciences.* New York: John Wiley & Sons, Inc., 1940.

20. Carter, H. A., and Potthoff, C. J., "Resuscitation," *J.A.M.A.*, 138: 23-24, (Sept. 4, 1948).

21. Cary, R. J., "A Brief History of the Methods of Resuscitation of the Apparently Drowned," *Johns Hopkins Hospital Bulletin*, (Aug., 1913).

22. Chase, H. C., "Anoxia—Its Surgical Significance," *Surgery, Gynecology and Obstetrics*, 73: 105-120, (Aug., 1941).

23. Clark, D. T., "Complications Following Closed-Chest Cardiac Massage," *J.A.M.A.*, 176: 255-258, (April 29, 1961).

24. Corsan, George H., *Diving and Swimming Book*. New York: A. S. Barnes and Co., 1926.

25. Coryllos, P. N., "Mechanical Resuscitation in Advanced Forms of Asphyxia," *Surgery, Gynecology and Obstetrics*, 66: 698-721, (April, 1938).

26. Cousteau, J. Y. and Dumas, F., *The Silent World*. New York: Harper and Brothers, 1953.

27. Craig, A. B., Jr., "Underwater Swimming and Loss of Consciousness," *J.A.M.A.*, 176: 255-258, April 29, 1961.

28. Cumston, C. G., "A Short Historical Sketch on Death from Drowning," *Medical Record*, xcv: 232-36, (February 8, 1919).

29. Cureton, T. K., Jr., *How To Teach Swimming and Diving*. New York: Association Press, 1934.

30. Cureton, T. K., Jr., "Natural and Artificial Buoyancy, Flotation, and Body Balance in the Water," *Beach and Pool*, 7: 272, (Sept., 1933).

31. Cureton, T. K., Jr., "The Philosophy of Swimming Instruction," *Beach and Pool*, 5: 162-166, (May, 1931), 244-246, (June, 1931).

32. Cureton, T. K., Jr., *Warfare Aquatics*. Champaign: Stipes Publishing Company, 1943.

33. Cureton, T. K., Jr., *Physical Fitness Appraisal and Guidance*. St. Louis: C. V. Mosby Co., 1947.

34. Cureton, T. K., Jr., *Beginning and Intermediate National Y.M.C.A. Progressive Aquatic Tests*. New York: Association Press, 1942.

35. Cureton, T. K., Jr., "Progress and Needs of the National Y.M.C.A. Aquatic Program," *Journal of Physical Education*, (May-June, 1940).

36. Cureton, T. K., Jr., Brown, John, Jr. and Fuhrer, J. W., Editorial Committee, *The New Y.M.C.A. Aquatic Program*. New York: Association Press, 1938.

37. Davis, J. H., "Fatal Underwater Breath Holding in Trained Swimmers," *Journal Forensic Science*, 6: 301-306, (July, 1961).

38. Dawson, P. M., *Physiology of Physical Education*. Baltimore: Williams and Wilkins Company, 1935.

39. Dill, D. B., "Symposium on Mouth-to-Mouth Resuscitation," *J.A.M.A.*, 167: 317-319, May 17, 1958.

40. Drinker, C. K., "The Functions of the Nerves in Lungs and Thoracic Wall," *Am. Rev. of Tuberculosis*, 58: 1-14, (July, 1948).

41. "Drowning Superstitions," *Science Magazine*, 18: (Dec. 4, 1891).

42. Duffner, Gerald J., "Medical Problems Involved in Underwater Compression and Decompression," *Clinical Symposia*, 10: 100-110, July-August, 1958.

43. Dull, C. E., Metcalf, H. C. and Brooks, W. D., *Modern Physics*. New York: Henry Holt & Co., 1955.

44. Edwards, L. F., *Concise Anatomy* Philadelphia: The Blakiston Co., 1947.

45. Empleton, B. E., Chairman, *The New Science of Skin and SCUBA Diving*. New York: Association Press, 1962.

46. Eve, F. C., "Resuscitation of the Drowned Today," *J.A.M.A.*, 124: 964-967, (April 1, 1944).

47. "Fatal Diving Injuries," New York: Metropolitan Life Insurance Co. Press, *Statistical Bulletin*, Vol. 20, No. 6, (June, 1939).

48. Fincham, Dr., "Insensibility from Attempted Drowning; Recovery after Two Hours by the Marshall Hall Method, with Other Treatment," *Lancet*, ii: 287, (Sept. 17, 1859).

49. Flagg, P. J., *The Art of Resuscitation*. New York: Reinhold Publishing Corp., 1944.

50. Fowler, W. S., "Breaking Point of Breath Holding," *Journal Applied Physiology*, 6: 539, (1954).

51. Friemann, "The Question of Sudden Drowning in Perforation of the Tympanic Membrane," *Deutsche med. Wchnschr.*, 1890-1891, (Nov. 13, 1936).

52. Friermood, H. T., Editor, *New YMCA Aquatic Workbook*. New York: Association Press, 1958, with revisions in 1960, 1961, 1962, 1964.

53. Frost, J., *The Art of Swimming*, New York: P. W. Gallaudet, 1818.

54. Gonzales, T. A., Vance, M. and Helpern, M., *Legal Medicine and Toxicology*, New York: D. Appleton Century Co., 1940.

55. Gordon, A. S., et al., "Manual Artificial Respiration," *J.A.M.A.*, 144: 17: 1447-1452 (December 23, 1950).

56. Gordon, A. S., "Manual Artificial Respiration," *What's New*—Abbott Laboratories, 165: 11-18 (February, 1952).

57. Gordon, A. S., Fainer, D. C., Ivy, A. C., "Artificial Respiration," *J.A.M.A.*, 144: 17: 1455-1464 (December 23, 1950).

58. Gordon, A. S., et al., "Mouth-to-Mouth Versus Manual Artificial Respiration for Children and Adults," *J.A.M.A.*, 167: 320-328 May 17, 1958.

59. Goss, G. E., *Life Saving*. New York: Association Press, 1916.

60. Goss, George E., "Life Saving." Unpublished Graduation Thesis, Springfield College, Springfield, Massachusetts, 1913.

61. Gabrielson, B. W., *Facts on Drowning Accidents*. Georgia: University of Georgia Printing Department, 1956.

62. Guyton, A. C., *Medical Physiology*, 2nd Edition. Philadelphia: W. B. Saunders Co., 1956.

63. Hall, J. N., *Lost Island*. Boston: Little, Brown & Co., 1944.

64. Hall, M., *Prone and Postural Respiration in Drowning, and Other Forms of Apnœa or Suspended Respiration*. London: J. Churchill, 1857. Also, *Medical Times › and Gazette*, 2: 425-26, (Oct. 24, 1857).

65. Hall, M., "Rules for Restoring the Drowned," *Lancet*, ii: 124, (Aug. 2, 1856).

66. Hall, M., "The Danger of All Attempts at Artificial Respiration Except in the Prone Position," *Lancet*, i: 134-35, (Feb. 7, 1856).

67. Harrison, W., "A Brief Historical Review of the Employment of a Bellows as a Means of Inducing Artificial Respiration During the 300 Years Which Elapsed Between A.D. 1530-1830." *Detroit Medical Journal*, xvi: 341-55, (Aug., 1916).

68. Henderson, Yandell, "Fundamentals of Asphyxia," *Journal of American Medical Association*, 101: 261-66, (July 22, 1933). Also, *American Journal of Public Health*, 23: 1192-93, (Nov., 1933).

69. Horton, B. T. and Gabrielson, M. A., "Hypersensitiveness to Cold: A Condition Dangerous to Swimmers," *Research Quarterly*, 11: 119-125, (Oct., 1940).

70. Howe, M. A. DeWolfe, *The Humane Society of the Commonwealth of Massachusetts*, Boston: The Riverside Press, 1918.

71. Karpovich, P. V., "Duration of Submersion in Drowning and Recovery," *Swimming Pool Data and Reference Annual*, 8: 66-67, (1940).

72. Karpovich, P. V., *Adventures in Artificial Respiration*. New York: Association Press, 1953.

73. Karpovich, P. V., "Ingenuity in Artificial Respiration," *Air Force*, (Jan., 1944).

74. Karpovich, P. V., "Methods of Artificial Respiration," *The Physical Educator*, 2: 112-115, (Feb. 1942).

75. Karpovich, P. V., "Problems in Drowning," *Journal of Physical Education*, 31: 87, (July, Aug., 1934).

76. Karpovich, P. V., "The Best Method of Artificial Respiration," *Research Quarterly*, 12: 50-59, (Mar., 1941).

77. Karpovich, P. V., "Water in the Lungs of Drowned Animals," *Archives of Pathology*, 15: 828-33, (June, 1933).

78. Karpovich, P. V., *Physiology of Muscular Activity*. Philadelphia: W. B. Saunders Co., 1959.

79. Keith, A., *Drowning, In A System of Surgery* by Choyce, C. C. and Beattie, J. M., New York: Funk & Wagnalls Co., Vol. 1, (1912).

80. Keith, Sir Arthur, "Three Hunterian Lectures on the Mechanism Underlying the Various Methods of Artificial Respiration Practiced Since the Foundation of the Royal Humane Society," *Lancet*, 1: 745-749, (May 13, 1909). *Ibid.*, 1: 825-828, (March 20, 1909). *Ibid.*, 895-899, (March 27, 1909).

81. Kouwenhoven, W. B., Jude, J. R., Knickerbocker, G. G., "Closed-Chest Cardiac Massage," *J.A.M.A.*, 173: 1064-1067, (July 9, 1960).

82. Lanoue, F. R., "Some Facts on Swimming Cramps," *Research Quarterly*, 21: 153, 1950.

83. Lanoue, F. R., *Drownproofing*. Englewood Cliffs, N. J.: Prentice-Hall, Inc., 1963.

84. Lanoue, F. R., Keyes, L. and Welser, L., "An Improved Technique in the Use of Inflated Pants as Life Preservers," *Journal of Health and Physical Education*, 14: 494-496, (Nov., 1943).

85. Lilly, John C., *Man and Dolphin*. Garden City, N. Y.: Doubleday & Co., Inc., 1961.

86. Lloyd, Frank S., Deaver, G. G. and Eastwood, F. R., *Safety in Athletics*. Philadelphia: W. B. Saunders Company, 1936.

87. Lougheed, D. W., Janes, J. M. and Hall, G. E., "Physiological Studies in Experimental Asphyxia and Drowning," *Canadian M.A.J.*, 40: 423-428, (May, 1939).

88. Manual Artificial Respiration Studies, *Journal of Applied Physiology*, 416: 403-495 (December, 1951).

89. The New Zealand Surf Life-Saving Association, *Official Handbook*, 3rd ed., Wellington: McKenzie, Thornton, Cooper, Ltd., 1945.

90. Nicholls, C. P. L., *Beach Water Safety*, Los Angeles: Department of Playground and Recreation, Mimeographed, 1939.

91. Olson, L. N., *Prevention, First Aid and Emergencies*. Philadelphia: W. B. Saunders Co., 1946.

92. Pohl, H. F., "History of the Surfboard," *Beach and Pool*, 20: 8-9, (Feb., 1946).

93. Pohl, H. F., "Lifesaving with the Surfboard," *Beach and Pool*, 18: 10-12, (Nov., 1944).

94. Pohndorf, Richard H., *Camp Waterfront Programs and Management*. New York: Association Press, 1960.

95. Potthoff, C. J., "Policy Changes Cited in Resuscitation Report," *The Reporter*, 6: 1-2, (Sept., Oct., 1948).

96. "Prevent Summer Drownings from Small Boats," New York: Metropolitan Life Insurance Co. Press, *Statistical Bulletin*, Vol. 20, No. 5, (May, 1939).

97. The Royal Life Saving Society, *Handbook of Instruction*. 21st ed., London: The Royal Life Saving Society, 1946.

98. Russo, E. and Arienzo, F., "Risks of Hyperventilization Before Swimming Underwater," *British Medical Journal*, 5239: 1596, (June 3, 1961).

99. Sachs, Frank, *The Complete Swimmer*, 3rd ed., London: Methuen & Co., Ltd., 1929.

100. Safar, P., et al., "Ventilation and Circulation With Closed Chest Cardiac Massage in Man," *J.A.M.A.*, 176: 574-576, (May 20, 1961).

101. Safar, Peter, and McMahon, Martin C., *Resuscitation of the Unconscious Victim*, Springfield, Ill.: Charles C. Thomas, 1959.

102. Safar, Peter, "Ventilatory Efficacy of Mouth-to-Mouth Artificial Respiration," *J.A.M.A.*, 167: 335-341, May 17, 1958.

103. Safar, Peter, et al., "A Comparison of the Mouth-to-Mouth and the Mouth-to-Airway Methods of Artificial Respiration with the Chest-Pressure Arm-Lift Methods," *The New England Journal of Medicine*, 258: 671-677, April 3, 1958.

104. *The Safety and Advantages of a Simple, Automatically Cycling Resuscitator Which Provides Alternating Positive and Negative Pressures.* Cambridge, Mass.: J. E. Emerson Co.

105. Saklad, Meyer, *Inhalation Therapy and Resuscitation.* Springfield, Ill.: Charles C. Thomas, 1953.

106. Schafer, E. A., "Artificial Respiration in Man," *The Harvey Lectures, 1907-1908.* Philadelphia: J. B. Lippincott Co., 1909.

107. Schafer, E. A., "Artificial Respiration in Its Physiologic Aspects," *J.A.M.A.*, 51: 801-803, (Sept. 5, 1908).

108. Schafer, E. A., "Description of a Simple and Efficient Method of Performing Artificial Respiration in the Human Subject, Especially in Cases of Drowning, To Which is Appended Instructions for the Treatment of the Apparently Drowned," *Transactions of the Royal Medical Chirurigical Society of London*, 87: 609-623, (1904).

109. Schwerma, H. and Ivy, A. C., "Safety of Modern Alternating Positive and Negative Pressure Resuscitators," *J.A.M.A.*, 129: 1256-1261, (Dec. 29, 1945).

110. Seaton, D. C., *Safety in Sports.* Englewood Cliffs, N. J.: Prentice-Hall, Inc., 1948.

111. Selye, H., *The Stress of Life.* New York: McGraw-Hill Book Co., Inc., 1956.

112. Shea, E. J., "Methods of Relieving Cramps in Swimming," *Athletic Journal*, 24: 45-46, (Oct., 1943).

113. Sheffield, T. W., "The Art of Surfboarding," *Beach and Pool*, 20: 10-11, (Sept., 1946).

114. Sheffield, T. W., "Evolution of Life Saving Services and Equipment," *Beach and Pool*, 13: 22-24, 26, (Feb., 1939). *Ibid.*, *Beach and Pool*, 13: 11, 24-25, (March 1939). *Ibid.*, *Beach and Pool*, 13: 14, 20-22, (April, 1939).

115. Sheffield, T. W., "Mechanics in Life Saving," *Beach and Pool*, 10: 10, 31, 33, (May, 1936). *Ibid.*, *Beach and Pool*, 10: 20, 22, (June, 1936).

116. Sheldon, W. H., *The Varieties of Human Physique.* New York: Harper and Brothers, 1940.

117. Sheldon, W. H., *The Varieties of Temperament.* New York: Harper and Brothers, 1944.

118. Shepard, F. B., Emery, K. O. and LaFond, E. C., "Rip Currents: A Process of Geological Importance," *The Journal of Geology*, 49: 337-369, (May, June, 1941).

119. Silvester, Henry R., "A New Method of Restoring Persons Apparently Drowned or Dead; and of Resuscitating Still-Born Children," *British Medical Journal*, 2: 576-579, (July 17, 1858).

120. Silvia, C. E., *Life Saving and Water Safety Bibliography.* Springfield: Unpublished Master's Thesis, Springfield College, 1940.

121. Silvia, C. E., "Life Saving in the War-Time Aquatic Program," *Scholastic Coach*, 16, 18, 39, (Oct. 1943), 44-48, (Nov., 1943).

122. Silvia, C. E. *Manual of Swimming Diving, Water Stunts, Life Saving and Water Safety.* Springfield: Privately published, 1953, 1957.

123. Simeons, A. T. W., *Man's Presumptuous Brain.* New York: E. P. Dutton and Co., Inc., 1961.

124. Sinclair, A. and Henry, W., *Swimming.* London: Longmans, 1916.

125. "Small Craft," *Safety Education Data Sheet No. 28.* Chicago: National Saefty Council, 1956.

126. Stack, H. J. and Siebrecht, E. B., *Education for Safe Living,* Englewood Cliffs, N. J.: Prentice-Hall, Inc., 1945.

127. Steedman, C., *A Manual of Swimming.* New York: Lockwood and Company, 1873.

128. Steinhaus, A. H., "Methods of Resuscitation Judged Physiologically," *Journal of Health and Physical Education,* 3: 38-39, (April, 1932).

129. Stone, D., *National Survey of the Young Men's Christian Association Life Saving Program,* Springfield: Unpublished Master's Thesis, Springfield College, 1937.

130. Sverdrup, H. A., Johnson, M. W. and Fleming, R. H., *The Oceans.* Englewood Cliffs, N. J.: Prentice-Hall, Inc., 1942.

131. Swann, H. G., Brucer, M., Moore, C. and Vezien, B. L., "Fresh Water and Sea Water Drowning; A Study of the Terminal Cardiac and Biochemical Events," *Texas Reports on Biology and Medicine,* 5: 423-437, (Winter, 1947).

132. Swann, H. G. and Spafford, N. R., *Texas Reports on Biology and Medicine,* 9: 356, 1951.

133. Tarr, R. S. and Engeln, D. Von, *New Physical Geography.* New York: The Macmillan Co., 1931.

134. Taylor, H. M., "Otitis and Sinusitis in the Swimmer," *J.A.M.A.,* 113: 891-895, (Sept. 2, 1939).

135. Thomas, Ralph, *Swimming.* London: Sampson Law, Marston and Company, 1904.

136. Thompson, S. A. and Birnbaum, G. L., "Asphyxial Resuscitation: The Phenomenon and Its Mechanism," *Jr. Thoracic Surgery,* 12: 624-637, (Oct., 1943).

137. Thompson, S. A. and Birnbaum, G. L., "Resuscitation in Advanced Asphyxia," *Surgery,* 12: 284-293, (Aug., 1942).

138. Thompson, S. A. and Rockey, E. E., "The Effect of Mechanical Artificial Respiration Upon Maintenance of the Circulation," *Surgery, Gynecology and Obstetrics,* 84: 1059-1064, (June, 1947).

139. Thompson, S. A. and Birnbaum, G. L., "The Phenomenon of Asphyxial Resuscitation," *Surgery, Gynecology and Obstetrics,* 74: 1078-1083, (June, 1942).

140. Thompson, S. A., "The Effect of Pulmonary Inflation and Deflation Upon the Circulation," *Jr. Thoracic Surgery,* 17: 323, 334, (June, 1948).

141. Thompson, T. C., "A Method of Artificial Respiration Especially Useful for the Paralyzed Patient," *J.A.M.A.,* 104: 4: 307-309 (January 26, 1935).

142. United States Navy, *Submarine Medicine Practice.* Washington: U.S. Government Printing Office, 1956. Nav Med P-5054.

143. Wallace-Dunlop, R. H., *Plate Swimming,* London: G. Routledge and Sons, 1876. (Contains first descriptions of flippers and nose clip.)

144. Weingarten, C. H. and Taubenhaus, L. J., "Training of Rescue Personnel Closed-Chest Cardiac Resuscitation," *The New England Journal of Medicine,* 270: 1396-1399, (June 25, 1964).

145. Whittenberger, J. L., editor, *Artificial Respiration.* New York: Harper & Row, 1962.

146. Wittmaack, K., "Sudden Death from Drowning Following Perforation of the Tympanic Membrane," *Deutsche med. Wchnschr.,* 62: 1329-1330, (Aug. 14, 1936).

Index